This Demi-Paradise

A WESTCHESTER DIARY

BY MARGARET HALSEY

Simon and Schuster ⚬ New York ⚬ 1960

c. 1

d7-13-60-nyb
HR
SEP 8 '60

In memory of Don Hollenbeck,
a man of honor

"This other Eden, demi-paradise . . ."
—SHAKESPEARE, *Richard II*

A charming fictional diary of a witty woman's life in suburbia. She fully appreciates the advantages of her life but recognizes its drawbacks.

January 3rd ❧ Take it for all in all, I rather dislike sociologists, so I could never accept a sociologist's description of myself as being "in conflict with my environment." I am not in conflict with my environment, because my environment does not know it is in a fight.

But it did occur to me on New Year's Eve—when I was doing the kind of stocktaking one does on that occasion—that the house has been very quiet in these years since Cora began going to school all day, and the typewriter stands unused, in the daytime, in Harry's cluttered little box of a study off the living room.

I have often heard it said that solitary children dream up make-believe companions with fanciful names like Snoopsie-Tootsie (although my own only child has never had such a companion that I knew of). Since I am a solitary adult during the daytime, why should I not have an imaginary companion called Ignis Fatuus or You-Over-There? All I know about Ignis is that he or she is a quivering mass of sensitiveness and receptivity . . .

❧*1*

January 4th ❧ When I was very young, I used secretly to pretend to myself that I had one of those beautiful, evocative names like "Elaine of the white hands" or "Deirdre of the sorrows." But perhaps it is just as well that I never seriously committed myself to that type of identification, for now that I am in the middle years, I would have to be called "Helen of the slight tendency to embonpoint."

I got to the subject of nomenclature because my mind was drifting idly backward to the morning's shopping.

The chunky metal superstructure above the one-story building bears the heraldic legend "Finast."

The sign over the plate-glass windows says "First National Stores."

But I always think of the place as "Plethora, Incorporated."

It was busy this A.M. I found a little backwater away from the nosing, questing carts and tried to remember whether Cora is still on the frankfurter kick. (Will that "kick" locution be around next year, I wonder?) Beyond me, at the checkers' desks, the housewives of Suburbia were lined up like cows at milking time—patient, not visibly expectant, the carts with food piled in rounded pyramids suggesting udders upside down.

Recollecting, after a moment, that my daughter's aliment is currently the cream cheese and jelly sandwich (varied by almost nothing else), I got back into motion—shoulders just slightly hunched against an effect of the light that always makes me nervous. The windows of Plethora, Inc., are so big that, even partly obscured by signs in phosphorescent pink and green about dollar days, they let in a substantial amount of view.

The mercantile part of our suburb is flat, so it is a view of sky with silhouettes of bare trees which, when in leaf, are blocky and mature—survivors from forty or fifty years ago when this area was given over to farms. In front of the building is a broad cement highway, and strong winter sunlight, animated with the glint and flash of wheeled traffic, pours into the front of the store. But the windows in front are the only fenestration. The back of the structure is lit with fluorescent tubes, which have the kind of luminosity that no doubt prevails inside a milk of magnesia bottle. Right in the middle of the store, these two kinds of light meet like ignorant armies clashing by day, and if there is such a thing as brilliant dismalness, this is it.

Resolutely shaking off aesthetic qualms, I moved with my fellow suffragettes down the aisles that always look to me like the stacks in a sort of giant food library. How impossible it is in the United States ever to get very far away from reminders of eating! Snack bars and chili joints on the highways, pizzerias on the back roads, pop corn in vast containers in the movies, slender hands on television pouring instant custard mix, four-color advertisements of caloric intake in all but the most resolutely intellectual magazines.

And in the supermarkets, twenty feet of soft drinks, fifty feet of vegetables . . .

"This is my own, my native land," I reflected, "and the Horn of Plenty is blasting me right out of my seat."

Suddenly I thought of the answer to all this opulence.

Lepers.

A row of lepers hunkered down on the pavement outside—lion-faced, greasy begging bowls held between the stumps where their hands used to be, winter wind whistling through their rags. There would be a challenge to togetherness! There, in fact, would be a stable, solid point of reference on which all this privilege could pivot—being properly appreciated by contrast.

The idea pleases me, but I shall keep it securely locked up in the privacy of this diary. When the Men of Merchandise find out that I want something, they always give it to me; and I can already see the sales promotion throwaway on my doorstep, intimating that the Safeway, the Food Fair, the Acme, the Grand Union and the Daitch-Shopwell lepers are mere malingerers and hangnail cases, and that if I want to see a really colossal falling-off, I must look at the beggars in front of the A & P.

But the American supermarket is no place for whimsy. Tinker Bell, for instance, would have found it rough going in the First National this morning, for the ceiling was thickly sown with banners announcing the start of a contest. The prize is a complete set of dishes—illustrated on the banners—and it can be secured by scaling some parlous hurdle like filling in the nickname of Dwight David Eisenhower.

I checked my list; saw that I had gotten everything; and wheeled my cart past the rack with the stockings, the stand with the house plants, the separate shelves with the drugs, the bin with the special on olives, the display of encyclopaedias, and the offering of children's books and phonograph records. I had just taken my place at the end of a long line, when a checker unhooked a chain and opened up a new alley. I darted into it like a guppy in an aquarium.

The checker was an unripe male organism of the type the newspapers refer to as a "youth." The weary knowledgeableness with which he tore off the ribbon from the cash register and dropped it into the brown paper bag suggested the French marquisate at its most overblown;

but I had a feeling that if challenged, he would not have been able to produce the nickname of Dwight David Eisenhower. Embracing my packages, I approached the massive, chromium-sheathed door. Suddenly, over the steady, uninflected chatter of cash registers, the Muzak went on. It was violins in unison—three million of them, apparently—playing *The Lorelei*.

> *"Ich weiss nicht, was soll es bedeuten,*
> *Dass ich so traurig bin . . ."*

> "I know not how it happens
> That I am so sad . . ."

January 7th ❧ "Mommy!"

The light, clear voice floats down the stairs and automatically my ear picks up the timbre of confidence and serenity.

"Does anyone want to kiss me good night?"

Harry and I look at each other over the Scrabble board. We are in a perfect, unflawed unity of feeling about the nine-year-old on the floor above. Climbing the stairs in front of my husband, I reflect that although the authorities who appear so ubiquitously in the Sunday papers and the magazines agree that children need love, social convention—actually—decrees that that love should be given very little verbal expression.

It is only allowed to find its way tortuously out through the back door (as it were) of humorous exasperation. Deprecating—minimizing—apologetic—one may allude jestingly to the children as "the little monsters" and describe with laughter how much trouble they are. But there is no sanction for mentioning the fragile, snowdrop purity of the napes of their necks or the splendid blaze of welcome in their eyes (like the hilltop beacons on Midsummer Night) when they are glad to see you.

If I do say so, we have Cora's room rather nicely fixed up. *"Alles für die Kinder,"* as the German immigrants used to say. The living room in our house looks like the English department office in a rather hard-up liberal college. There are the same faded chintzes, the same white bookcases with long, slightly sagging shelves. Bookcases turning a bit yellow, for Harry and I are not Do-It-Yourself people. What we cannot afford to have done by upholsterers, painters, carpenters, master electricians, brain surgeons and embalmers, goes undone. But in Cora's room the floral patterns are not faded and the bookcase is of a Euclidean straightness.

She was in bed.

"Look," she said, pointing to a mound under the pink blanket. "The Pink Puffy Omelet from Outer Space."

The mound heaved, and from underneath, stifled but unmistakable, came the hoarse, plangent cry of a Siamese cat. It was the voice of Young Cat—the one we sometimes refer to as the fur-bearing bluejay.

"Let him go," I said.

"In a minute," she answered. "I'm punishing him for chewing the lace on my crinoline."

"Now," I said.

Cora laid a slender hand on the bulge under the blanket. I looked at the hand and said, "Cora!"

She seized my meaning instantly. Laughter and apprehension struggled for possession of her features.

Harry had seen the hand, too.

"Did you have a bath?" he asked.

Cora's outraged innocence showed that Penrod Scho-field is far from being an outmoded literary creation.

"You can just go in and look at the . . ."

Remembering that she is supposed to clean out the tub, she stopped and clapped a hand over her mouth. But suddenly recalling, also, that the state of that hand was under investigation by a Parento-Kefauver Committee, she put it behind her and looked confused.

Harry took off his glasses and pointed them at her.

"I know," he said. "Just as you sat down in the tub, a cowboy came in and said, 'Reach!' So that's why only the bottom half of you is clean."

"Daddy!"

The protest was purely mechanical, the tone being one of undiluted admiration.

"On your way, lady," I said, and pulled back the covers.

A brown and *café-au-lait* projectile arced through the air, lit briefly at the door, and was down the stairs with an incredibly rapid scrabble of claws on the uncarpeted treads. This did not represent, however, a consensus in the cat population. Undisturbed by the turning back of the covers, Old Cat lay next to Cora's floating ribs—eyes closed, forepaws turned back on themselves in soft abandon, only the whiskers sticking out briskly from the general contour of defenseless slumber.

I looked a little enviously at this pageant of relaxation.

"Lymph, in thy orisons, be all my sins remembered," I murmured.

Cora had stiffened with protest at what she correctly deduced was an order to wash her face and hands, but when she saw her father engaged in the customary grown-up occupation of laughing at something that was not funny, she departed without comment for the bathroom.

"And clean out the tub, too," I called after her.

Cora has not had a permissive upbringing. When she was a very small baby, I read the books which describe in ominous terms what happens to children who have been frustrated and not allowed to develop, unimpeded, all their happy natural talents and instincts. And having read the books, I threw them out.

"I cannot," I said to Harry, "pass on to her something I did not have myself."

When I was growing up, martinets from West Point and disciplinarians from V.M.I. used to drop around and take lessons from my parents on how to break in the raw recruits. With that kind of background, I am no more able to be permissive and non-frustrating than I am able to steal bananas from a pushcart. If I were to try, I should be so unsure of myself, so flounderingly divorced from all my early beginnings, that Cora and I would both be miserable.

They tell me that permissiveness is now going out of fashion and discipline is coming back. Indeed, when I remarked at a dinner-party conversation last week that Harry and I have always been strict with Cora, a pert young thing replied carelessly, "Oh, everybody always says that. But when you actually see the children, no one has been strict with them at all."

I put on a haughty look.

"Perhaps I am not strict with Cora," I said, "but how do you account for the fact that I only got her back this afternoon from the S.P.C.C.?"

The theories about parenthood come and go, but I do

not in my heart of hearts feel it necessary to pay much attention to them. Not in a country where they can speak of a man as "fathering" the hydrogen bomb.

However, I was not thinking in this portentous vein when Cora returned from the bathroom, nose and cheeks shining with soap. (If she had not cleaned out the tub, she had at least made sloshing noises to suggest that she had.) From the slightly troubled look in her blue-grey eyes, I realized she was up against the dilemma which so complicates the night life of children.

Every nerve and muscle was calling for sleep, but brain and imagination were at the stretch. What exciting event might happen if she let herself sink into cloddish slumber? . . . a fire in one of the houses on our street . . . a phone call . . . Mommy and Daddy having words . . . an unexpected visitor . . . something marvelous on television that THEY might summon her to see, it was so good . . . one of the neighbors being taken away in an ambulance. And she would miss it! (But the eyes are heavy, the eyelids like mattresses.)

On this day, too, there had been ice cream with chocolate sauce in the school lunchroom. And she had learned that her poem on wishing for the first crocus to come up was going to be printed on the children's page of the local newspaper. And looking at herself in the full-length mirror this morning, in the pink dress and the crinoline, she had been gratified with the reflected image.

It couldn't be right, could it? . . . for a segment of time so rich and distinctive just to be dropped in the wastebasket, as it were, and allowed to become faceless and uniform and lost in the procession of other days?

With a faint feeling of betraying a colleague, I crossed to

her desk and turned out the light, so that the only illumination came from the bathroom across the hall.

"Slide in very, very gently," I said, "so as not to disturb Old Cat."

Our cats can be slept with, for they do not go outdoors. They started life in a city apartment, and if they were ever to get beyond our suburban threshold, they would be merely a bit of protein in the diet of the nearest Doberman Pinscher.

Cora slipped down and curled around the cat. Harry bent over to kiss her, and then I kissed her—feeling the ache of time passing as I rested one hand lightly on the bony hip and remembered when she was a little thing with bracelets of fat around her wrists and a small body dimpled like a pond in the rain.

Old Cat exhaled asthmatically and Cora clutched him.

"C'n I have an English bike?" she asked in a voice already growing remote.

Harry and I answered simultaneously.

"No," I said. "They cost too much."

" 'May I,' not 'Can I,' " Harry said.

Harry is a regional planner, having come to that profession via architecture. He is a purist, a voracious reader, a grasper of abstract concepts, and would be a true-blue intellectual except for one thing—he never uses the prefix "crypto" about people he does not like. Harry served in the Merchant Marine in World War Roman Numeral Two, and the simple abuse of the fo'c'sle is good enough for him.

Cora was already asleep. In the half light, I could see the phenomenal eyelashes lying like small dark animals along her cheek. Harry and I smiled at each other and, light of heart, went back downstairs to our Scrabble.

January 11th ❧ My husband and I would certainly be described by the casual observer as people who have a church affiliation, although—when I think of the religious observances of my childhood—I can only conclude that one of those two words must be wrong. I still remember that when I was about seven or eight years old, a little French girl moved into a house on our street; and when I asked her what religion she was—it was one of the first questions, in those days—she said she and her family were "fwee-thinkers."

Had I known what a "fwee-thinker" really was, I should have departed from there in a hurry, so as not to be struck down by lightning when the Deity blasted this little anti-clerical from the face of the earth. But I somehow concluded—was there something a shade defiant in her manner?—that "fwee-thinker" was French for one of those sects from the wrong side of the track who thought that God Is Love and did not know that (*au contraire!*) God Is Stately. Hence it was in a spirit of conscious magnanimity that I said, "Let's play."

My daughter Cora, of course, is rapidly being trained not to make any such mistake. Cora goes to a low-calorie, salt-free, modern, liberal Sunday school, and she has been dunked in comparative religion ever since she could say, "Gautama Buddha." Like a good many Americans on my particular level, I left the stained-glass windows and the mystery cult behind me a long time ago; and it was not until I had a child to bring up that I gave any thought at all to the problem of systematized ethics and how to inculcate them into the young.

In the beginning, I was enthusiastic about this non-candle-burning church. For an organized religion, it has an exceptional history—which I assumed it was trying to live up to. After World War I, the membership was outspokenly pacifist; and a certain well-known trade-union of warriors picketed it, caused editorials to be written branding it as "Bolshevist," and organized rallies to denounce it. Rallies that were very well attended.

Somewhat later, it was the first and only Caucasian fane hereabouts to attract and welcome a few members of the Negro middle class. That was back in the days when nobody dreamed of such a thing as a Supreme Court decision, and even the most enlightened people got pink in the face when asked how they would like their daughters to marry one.

There is still a handful of parishioners—the old-timers —who want the church to take a stand on controversial matters, but they are sadly outnumbered. Nowadays the only way you can tell it is a liberal church is that the women's hats are so terrible. *Sic transit gloria spiritus.*

Unlike me, Harry was not disappointed in these apostates, since he had not looked for anything in the first place. Harry really *is* a "fwee-thinker"—a point he illustrated with admirable succinctness only recently. Cora had come in with an uncooperative Young Cat plastered to her diaphragm underneath her jersey, and when I adjured her to let the animal go, she replied that she was the Spartan boy with the fox gnawing at his vitals.

"That's what he got for going to church," Harry said. "There are no foxholes in atheists."

Nevertheless, he teaches in Sunday school, works hard on getting up the material for his classes, and sometimes comes home with grinny corners on his mouth when things have gone swimmingly. He has the ninth grade—a band of brothers and a happy few who are apt to err on the side of impulsiveness rather than preciosity and polish.

12

For my own part, I give out books in the Sunday-school library and help out with mailings, typing and phone calls.

And why?

Why take this trouble, when our feelings are so often detached and ironic?

Like most people, Harry and I got into the situation first and thought up the rationale later; but the rationale was very simple. We do not want Cora to assume that Western ethics is a whimsical arrangement of debits and credits thought up by her father and mother. We should like her to have the sense that morality is institutionalized, that it is a summing up of human experience involving other people besides her parents and other generations besides the ones now living. For this desirable end, we are willing to pay the stiffish price of being included— even if only as a couple of anonymous statistics—in that great theological burp, the so-called "return to religion."

I see that I have written all these paragraphs without having mentioned the Reverend Doctor Aspirin. That is not, of course, the name by which you look him up in the phone book; but it is the name he will go under in our household until such time as he is Ennobled By Suffering —a transmutation which is not immediately in prospect.

One remembers reading in Victorian novels about the good-looking minister who was a great favorite with the ladies, though regarded as sissified and emasculate by the men. But the men, of course, could not say so because of The Cloth. In our feebler times, that kind of curé is no longer condescended to by the male parishioners. On the contrary, Dr. Aspirin's study door is perpetually being knocked on by executives and businessmen whose nerves are quivering on the edge of collapse. The years like great black oxen tread them down, and they cannot fight off the suspicion that their work has been "made" work and that just as there are paper tigers, so there are paper jobs. *Their* jobs.

To breadwinners in this situation, Dr. Aspirin is exquisitely sympathetic. No one could listen more understandingly or interject more meaningfully. The dominie knows what is wrong with our society, and says so. Madison Avenue . . . the cheapening effect of the mass market. . . .

> "Oh, beautiful for specious skies
> And amber drinks of Scotch . . ."

The vicar is cognizant of, and fluent about, them all.

But in the end, his advice always comes down to God's being on the side of the big corporations, and the truly brave person's being willing to come to terms with this fact. (Is it peculiar to our times, I wonder—the rebellion that starts out genuinely enough but ends up with the apple cart not only upright, but actually nailed to the floor?)

Nobody, naturally, is going to ask a man of Dr. Aspirin's talents to live like a mendicant friar; and it is pretty well understood by the congregation that the pastor needs the peace and quiet of the woods and the inspiration of the furtive hepatica in order to get his sermons written. So, although the rest of us live apprehensively among our well-grown evergreens—awaiting the rising tide of highways, stores and poured concrete which will eventually engulf us—the Doc is domiciled a fur piece down the road with a long view and a meadow for his Irish setters to gallop in. It takes him twenty-five minutes of fast driving to make the meetings of the Men's Club and the bedsides of the dying.

But these are the carping criticisms of the pastor's intimates. He has an enviable reputation, particularly on the score of juvenile delinquents, in the handling of whom he is esteemed to be a virtuoso. All up and down our constellation of townships, whenever somebody celebrates a fourteenth birthday by raping the postman, Dr. Aspirin is sent for to dispel the murk of savagery and create a livable, breathable atmosphere of reasonableness and tendresse. "The kids," as Harry remarked, "all go to reform school in the end, but the ones who are talked to by Aspirin get a hell of a send-off."

Children who are not in trouble seem to interest the vicar somewhat less. The Sunday-school curriculum is planned—and the Sunday-school committee meetings attended—largely by unpicturesque nobodies and a handful of characters who were for Roosevelt before Chicago.

Postscriptum: Of course, all these lucubrations about the church really started because I have to be one of a panel of three at the Sundays at Seven meeting six weeks hence. This is a discussion group which is going to consider a whole series of Biblical texts and ethical injunctions that have a bearing on modern life, and the evening I have been chosen for is "Love thy neighbor." I kissed the hems of garments and pleaded to be assigned some topic I am better at, like "Thou shalt not commit adultery," but to no avail.

What shall I talk about?

If I know contemporary life, this discussion—even in

our semi-egghead church—is going to be fuller of idiot kindness than an institutional ad.

How to come to grips?

Can one come to grips?

January 17th ❧ They may say what they like about the suburbs, but when there is a snowfall, we have our interlude of breathlessness and magic. There was six inches of snow on the ground when we woke up this morning, and it was still falling. When I went into the dining room, the light coming up into the room from the lawn was all pearliness and texture, as if one had walked into a painting. The steady downward motion of the flakes hypnotized, and the little hesitant swirls in the angle of the porch only served to accent the compelling, purposeful sweep beyond. Silent, silken-flowing motion and the wonderful irradiated grey of the light . . . I had to hit myself on the head to get started on the practical affairs of the day.

There are people in our neighborhood who complain about the snow, saying it makes trouble and is inconvenient and a nuisance; but to my mind a heavy snowfall is one of the few *real* happenings that is left to us. In this era of public relations—when the doctored or fabricated event is the norm, and headlines are administered like hypodermics—a heavy snowfall is one of the things that nobody can tamper with. Suddenly, in a life of pastel garbage pails and rainbow-hued plastics, there is a merciful absence of color. Suddenly, in an environment where canned music enlivens even the precincts of savings and loan associations, there is a blessed absence of sound.

At least, there is an absence of sound for the Fitzgibbons

family and its neighbors, for we live on a hill, and with one of these all-day snowfalls, everything stops. Harry went off to the station this morning on foot, and there is, of course, no school. On such a day—with bare hedge, leafless tree, garage roof and withered flower stalk all transfigured by snow—it would have been highly unsuitable, almost unethical, to have cleaned up the cellar a little. (As I had been planning.) So I threw some kindling and logs on top of the rather messy ashes in the fireplace, moved the typewriter into the living room, and here I am writing my diary in front of the cheerful blaze like an eighteenth-century gentlewoman.

Old Cat and Young Cat have knitted themselves into a single pile of fur, as Siamese do, and are fast asleep on the hearth-rug. I have a steaming cup of coffee on the table and a slightly stale Danish. . . . it calls to mind a favorite quote of Harry's from Homer Smith's *Man and His Gods:*

"Unhappiness, whether avoidable or not, too frequently comes in large pieces. But happiness is generally as fine-grained as life itself, and so intimately intermixed with living that it can be extracted from breathing, eating, sleeping, waking . . ."

Cora came in half an hour ago to get some dry gloves. Her skinny little figure was whitened from head to foot with caked snow and her cheeks looked like a small Aurora Borealis.

"Having a good time, Lady Agatha?" I asked.

"Oh, Mommy!" she said fervently. "I'm so glad to be *me!*"

My heart simply folded its wings like a dove (under the prosaic dark-green knit) and said, "Well, friends, this is the summit."

"When I think," Cora went on, looking at me radiantly, "of all those thousands and thousands of women, and all those millions and millions of seeds, I feel so *lucky!*"

I could have hugged her to extinction, but she was clearly not in the mood for embraces—besides, she was wet—so I merely said, "Just keep on talking like that, and you will not find your aged parents stepping into the bathroom to slash their wrists."

She gave me the glance which means that although I have elected to discourse in Aramaic, she can tell from my tone what I am saying. Then she ran out.

The snow has caught me with a somewhat barren larder, but there is a can of hash on the supply shelf that I can use for dinner, and I will make a chocolate cake. As to the wholesome, wholesome vegetables, the hell with them. We will forget about roughage and vitamins and just get nice and comfortably clogged up on carbohydrates.

Why am I so pleased with my snowstorm? I guess it is partly because everything is so beautiful in the snow, and partly that anything which defeats the automobile—and leaves it lifting its chilled paws one by one from the cold floor of the garage—pleases me. When we have a snowstorm, I realize that this great, booming, boastful, prosperous country is really nothing more than Stalag 17 on wheels.

January 24th 〜 Friend Cynthia came in this evening to borrow some thread and stopped to talk awhile.

Friend Cynthia lives just down the street. She is younger than I and very pretty. Russell, her husband, is a research chemist, and they have two small boys of whom the elder is so winning a child that Malthus himself would have said, "Let's have more of this." The younger, though by no means unappealing, has the most mulish and inflexible will I have ever come across and when I baby-sit with him (I with my ideas of discipline!) we fight each other to a standstill.

Cynthia and Harry and I were in desultory and rather inattentive converse when I happened to pick up some scraps of paper which Cora had left on the coffee table. She had been practicing her homework on them, and I was struck with how unformed her handwriting is. The capital letters wavered and fell like the spears at Thermopylae.

"When we were in the fourth grade," I said, "we would have been left back for handwriting like that."

I guess Harry was a little bored, which made him impatient.

He shrugged and said, "Fake nostalgia. You talk as if our generation were writing *Paradise Lost* in grammar school."

I drew myself up to my not very great height and spoke with acerbity.

"It just so happens, my good man, that some of us were."

Harry pulled his glasses down to the end of his nose and looked at me.

"It seems like yesterday," I said dreamily. "That day in the second grade when I threw down my pencil and said, 'By golly, I've got it! The thing to do is start with a preposition. *Of* Man's-first-disobedience-and-the-fruit/ Of-that-forbidden-tree-whose-mortal-taste/ Brought-death-into-the-world-and-all-our-woe . . .' "

Cynthia flung herself back on the sofa and laughed, but it was Harry I looked at. Harry cradled his torso with his arms, and I could tell from the expression on his face that the bonds of Hymen were not chafing him.

January 29th ✒ It was churlish weather yesterday—a cold, bleak winter day that justified everything city people say about living in the suburbs. I was sewing in the dining room; the house was oppressively quiet; and I was feeling lonely and left out of things, when suddenly the doorbell rang. Upon opening the front door, I was confronted by a handsome young woman of about thirty who instantly reminded me of a refrigerator. She was large and well built and porcelain-coated and ran with a small, quiet hum.

Or did she, with her height and her handsomeness, suggest a bell tower?—a campanile with the bells left out?—the Leaning Tower of Pisa straightened up?

At any rate, her smile was pleasant. She had the kind of teeth that dispose of peanut brittle as if it were farina.

"Good afternoon," she said equably and pointed to a thick notebook she was carrying, along with her purse, in the crook of her arm. "I'm from . . ."

She named a famous pollster.

"Mine eyes dazzle," I said, and moved back from the door with a welcoming gesture to invite her in.

If this personable young woman had one outstanding quality, it was imperviousness. In her well-bred way, she shared with the professional footballer a certain studied resistance to being bowled over. Nevertheless, it was apparent from the minute alteration of her face that, whatever the Mob Psychology courses at Vassar had prepared her for, quotations from the Elizabethans had not been included.

Actually, my comment was only partly satirical. The destinies of Americans are sealed, not by reason, logic, common sense or the indisputable shape of fact but by the dictates of opinion polls. And yet no pollster had ever come to our house to collect our opinions. One may try to rationalize. One may say that the people whose sentiments triumph on opinion polls have all the intellectual grasp of a chimpanzee with the falling sickness. Nevertheless, as I once remarked gloomily to Harry, it certainly makes you feel alienated from the culture when nobody comes to your house but friends.

At my invitation, the visitor seated herself with grace and composure on the sofa, and I mentally marked one up in her favor. The social commentators may insist until they are blue in the face that this is now a classless society, and that all former gradations and separations have been leveled down by the easy access to wall-to-wall carpeting. They are wrong. There are some people who still have manner in social situations, and there are a lot who do not —and no amount of pinch pleats for the formerly curtain-less can obscure the distinction.

"Why me?" I said curiously to the visitor.

I was feeling extremely grateful for the interruption to a lonely afternoon—Cynthia had taken the steam cars into the city—and, if I am to be completely honest with myself, I had the ineffably sweet sensation of having been singled out for special attention.

"How," I went on, "do you select which people you are going to call on? I know you don't do this door-to-door. Do you just close your eyes and stick pins in the telephone book?"

Once again there was the infinitesimal alteration of face. For a moment I thought the visitor was going to say, in the best roman-policier manner, "I'll ask the questions."

But she smiled and said, "We have our ways."

And there, of course, was where she lost me. I bristled inwardly and said to myself, "Who does she think she is? Mother Church?"

My poor innocent visitor, all unaware that she now had the Albigensian heresy on her hands, opened her notebook. She did not, however, begin to write. She merely fingered some white cards which were lying on the page.

"You have a lot of books," she said.

"It's just my remedial reading," I answered modestly.

She gave me the tiniest and most fleeting of smiles, as if to say that she recognized the phrase but had no time to dance upon the intellectual greensward.

"You're Mrs. Harry Fitzgibbons," she went on, glancing down at her notebook, "and this is 20 Simmonds Crescent."

I smiled, but said nothing.

She picked up one of the white cards and handed it to me. Scanning it briefly, I saw that it contained—in double columns, on each side—a long list of magazines.

Leaning forward to hand me a pencil, the visitor asked me to check the periodicals to which we subscribed.

"We don't subscribe to any," I replied.

She dropped the pencil.

"Why-I-never-heard-of-such-a-thing!" she exclaimed, all in one breath. Then the spacious and non-tendentious influence of social science reasserted itself and she added more judicially, "In an American family."

"It saves money."

"Oh."

She nodded understandingly, and then automatically glanced around the room. (Perhaps to see if we had the bailiffs in?)

"I get tired," I said, "of any given magazine. Coming in so regularly. Always the same."

In what may have been an unconscious gesture to gain time, my visitor stooped over and picked up the pencil.

"Actually," I went on, "I would really like a magazine to change its size, its shape and its politics about every third issue."

She was game. She smiled.

"Yes, I know what you mean," she said.

And I—in a sudden and possibly ignoble desire to be understood and to remove myself from the category of the unusual and the bizarre—continued.

"We do read magazines. We look at them in the public library."

I was about to add that we are frequenters of the public library, when Young Cat strolled into the room. The visitor looked pleased.

"Siamese," she said affectionately. "They're so beautiful."

Young Cat stopped in front of her, stretched fore and aft, sniffed briefly at the edge of her skirt, and then bounded lightly up to the table underneath the window.

"And of course," I remarked, "sometimes we get in one of those utterly reckless, *Atlantic Monthly* moods and buy one to read on the train."

"Did you used to subscribe to any?" the visitor asked.

I gave her a reassuring smile.

"How else would I know that I found them monotonous?"

"What magazines did you formerly . . . *what is that cat doing?*"

Young Cat was chewing industriously away on the ruffled organdy window curtain, and had he had lips, he would have been smacking them. Normally, confronted by such a sight, I would have leapt to my feet, snatched up the cat, cuffed him heartily while he held his ears down and yelled his hoarse, laryngical yell, and finally thrust him into the kitchen and slammed the door.

But the wish to daunt the Straight Tower of Pisa made me control myself and feign an elaborate calm.

"He's eating the curtains," I said casually, and did not add that they had been washed and ironed and I had forgotten, when I put them back up, to dust them with pepper. This forbidding condiment restricts Young Cat to his more normal diet of liver, fish and horsemeat.

I got up and approached him slowly. He crouched down and looked back and up at me over his shoulder, his eyes a blaze of cerulean blue in the chocolate mask of his face, his white teeth and pink tongue showing as he made noises like an Angry Young Man. He knew what was coming, but Young Cat can no more walk away from a tasty bit of un-peppered organdy ruffle than I can stick to a cottage-cheese diet when taken to dinner in a restaurant.

I picked him up and put him on my shoulder, but I did not anchor him firmly enough and he parachuted to the sofa. (Harry calls him the Flying Tiger because he has spent more time being airborne than Mrs. Roosevelt.) I plunged after him and caught him, but the edge of my skirt—made of unpressed pleats and voluminous—flicked across the visitor's notebook and knocked a card to the floor.

It was the work of a moment to thrust Young Cat into the kitchen, and on my way back to my chair I anticipated my guest and picked up the card.

Glancing down, I saw that it contained a list, like the other one, save that this list began

24

Gin
Vodka
Scotch
Rye
Bourbon
Sherry

"We do drink," I said, handing back the card, "but only the true, the blushful Hippocrene."

Her face was unresponsive.

"With beaded bubbles winking at the brim," I said, "and purple-stainèd mouth."

She made a tiny, impatient, dismissive motion with her head, and I felt that twinge of loneliness I get when I again become aware that the world is full of nothing but engineers and electronics experts—whereas I want it to be full of people who majored in English.

"What is this survey for?" I asked. "What are you trying to find out?"

She smiled.

"Oh, several things," she replied easily, and, opening her purse, took out a handkerchief which I saw was monogrammed.

The monogram suddenly made me aware of something that had been bothering me. My visitor wore a suit—she was the kind of woman who is born with a suit instead of a caul—but I could not see it very well under her coat. Her bag was expensive, however, and so were the shoes on her large, if slender, feet.

I gave her a smile which I hoped would be interpreted as inviting confidences.

"You're the wrong age to be doing this," I said. "You should either be a decayed gentlewoman of fifty or a young girl fresh out of Bennington and all aflame with devotion to motivational research."

There was the briefest possible flicker of response.

"Are you," I went on, "one of the executives who's trying out a new test?"

If Princess Margaret came over here and got a job behind the counter at Woolworth's, would she be outraged beyond any possibility of appeasement if some perceptive customer saw through her incognito?

My visitor was saved from having to reply by the ringing of the telephone.

I went out into the hall to answer it, and as soon as I picked up the receiver, an urgent female voice said, "Helen, for heaven's sake, did you forget? You were supposed to bring milk and cookies for the Brownies."

"Oh, my Lord!" I exclaimed penitently. "I'll pick up some at the store and be right down."

Briefly, I explained the situation to my vis-à-vis and started scrabbling through the coat closet.

She stood up—with, I noticed, the relieved and happy air of an egghead whose television set has just broken— and made swift but courtly adieux. As the door closed behind her, I went into the kitchen to look for the car keys. Young Cat greeted me from the stove, where he was sitting in a magnificent pose next to the pilot light. I took time out to pick him up and do a waltz step around the kitchen table.

"Always remember," I said to him, "never to tell them anything but your name, rank and serial number."

February 4th ❧ I do not know whether it is cultural conditioning or a basic glandular difference, but a man driving a car fast over old and ill-repaired macadam sits there with flashing eyes and distended nostrils—thinking in terms of Douglas Fairbanks, Sr., and saying exultantly to himself, "I'm holding her on the road!" A woman, on the other hand, driving at the same pace over the same road, merely thinks dismally, "Oh, gosh, it's bumpy!"

How it may be with other married couples, I do not know, but between Harry and me there is a constant and none too delicately expressed rivalry as to who is the better driver. When one of us backs the car into a parking space, and with a single expert twirl places the rear wheels exactly where they have to be, the congratulations of the other have just that note of excess which conveys incredulity and unflattering surprise.

It is Harry's contention when we go on long trips that my mind, while driving, is always on the scenery, on Cézanne, on Mont Saint-Victoire and on cubes in nature, and never on the road. It is my counter-contention that when Harry drives in traffic, he is always slewed completely around talking animatedly to the people in the back seat, while pedestrians go down before him like wheat before the scythe. Harry, indeed, considers an automobile as a sort of weapon—a kind of extra fist with which to menace other motorists whose normal self-respect he finds offensive. Conversely, Harry's complaint about me is that I wait until every last sloth, inchworm and veteran of the War of 1812 has crossed the road before I even begin to think of taking my pretty little landau out of neutral.

The other area in which our personalities clash is on the issue of neatness. I do not so much mind the fact that the top of Harry's dresser always looks like a plate of scrambled eggs, because that is upstairs and no one sees it but the family. But when I backed out of his little study off the living room the other night, I was moved to ask, "What were you doing in here, Planner? Shoeing horses?"

(A retroactive irritation swept over me because a woman I do not know very well had stopped in that afternoon to collect for the hospital, and the casualness and breezy informality of Harry's study—as seen through the open door—was not the kind they photograph for *House & Garden*.)

"Madame Anal-Erotic," he replied suavely. "Tell me about your toilet training."

Oh, there, Philip Wylie!

February 7th 〰 It seemed hot and stuffy in the house last night, so after I had finished the dinner dishes, I went out for a walk. It was a beautiful winter night, cold and still, with a planet compelling attention in the west and the bare branches of the trees making a sort of cushiony darker darkness against the less implacable sable of the sky. At intervals a street lamp shone down on the strong, squirrel grey of the tree trunks. The houses under the trees were superlatively inviting. Cradled in rhododendron, juniper and yew, they glowed with lamplight and showed the passer-by hospitable mantelpieces, bits of banister and flowery segments of bedroom wall.

"I wish I didn't know who lived here," I thought. "I wish I could look at these lamplit houses on a winter night and think, 'What a noble race built these! What a talent for self-government they have! How far from the primeval ooze they have come!' "

Of course, in the dark, I could not see the television

aerials through the tree branches, and in our hilly streets —with everybody shored up by embankments and retaining walls—my angle of vision did not include the flickering bluish screens.

Television . . .

Not, perhaps, the primeval ooze, but certainly the dullest thing since Victor Hugo.

February 8th ✺ When Harry and I and Bottomless Cora—so called because she has absolutely no fanny— play Parchesi, my husband and my daughter gang up on me. They do not send each other's men home, but unite in sending mine home instead. This agreement between them is so completely automatic and instinctive that it does not even need to be verbalized. One speaking glance will do. For my own part, I am not disposed to tiptoe with reverence around the venerated name of Sigmund Freud. If it took the old gentleman until 1880 to discover that what goes on between father and nine-year-old daughter makes Venusberg look like a handshake, he must have been goldbricking.

February 10th ✺ Oh, that I knew some Gaelic curse of surpassing malevolence! Some ruthless and utterly effective incantation that would shrivel and wither and blast. . . . The squirrels have eaten my crocus and scilla bulbs. Seven dollars' worth. I looked out the window this morning, while waiting for the iron to heat, and there were two squirrels sitting up on their hind legs among the dead leaves and munching away at flower bulbs like Cora eating an apple after school.

I ran outside and looked at all the spots where I had put in clumps of bulbs. It was the same with each—the bulbs had been dug up and partly chewed. Our yard is nothing but trees and shade, so all we can grow are mossy tombstones and funerary urns; but I did think I might have a few little blossoms in the spring, before the leaves came out. I called up several of the neighbors who, like Thoreau, "can make the earth say beans instead of grass." They have, however, nothing to recommend but resignation. Mrs. John Q. Taxpayer is the toy, the sport, the idle plaything of any local rodent who happens to feel the nudge of appetite.

And to think that I used to look at the silvery undulations of those plumy tails and find them attractive!

February 13th ❧ Had a cup of tea with Friend Cynthia this afternoon and wondered as I often have before why people are so condescending about vicarious satisfactions. They are, after all, satisfactions. I take a vicarious satisfaction in Cynthia's looks, and *vic*arious does not necessarily mean *prec*arious. Cynthia is tall and willowy and blond, with lovely symmetrical features; whereas it is usually said of me that my face is redeemed by animation.

This, of course, means that there is one thing I will never be very good at.

Lying in state.

Naturally, there is more to Cynthia than looks. It is odd how one thoughtlessly assumes that a pretty young woman will not be very strong on either character or brains. Does form suggest function? Does the flowerlike appearance automatically suggest the flowerlike life? At any rate, it is misleading so far as Cynthia is concerned, for—though she is the mother of two small children—she gets up at five o'clock several mornings a week to paint.

Despite there being quite a difference in our ages, Cynthia and I have proved to be extremely companionable. We are, for one thing, the only political Know-Somethings on this street (except for our husbands, of course). But there is an even more basic attitude involved. Sir Osbert Sitwell once said, on an American television show, "I like speech to be bitter as a blade." This sentiment certainly did not win Sir Osbert a large and slavish following in Eisenhower's America, but Cynthia and me he took right along with him. We both have a dislike of anything that is too soft.

I must really bring this to a stop. It is nearly dinner time, and Young Cat and Old Cat are weaving restlessly around the legs of my chair, making that Siamese plaint which can only be described as sounding like a Southeast-Asian bagpipe.

The thought of getting dinner reminds me that Cynthia and I agreed this afternoon that we are sated to the point of nausea with colorfulness in everyday tools and equipment. The pink-handled broom, the lemon-yellow dishpan, the pale-blue formica kitchen-table top, the brilliant red measuring spoons, the bronze-gold canisters . . .

The green-and-orange lawnmower, the whole gamut of hues in plastic toys, the orchid colored bicycle, the variegated saucepans, the confection-tinted toilet paper, the tawny stove and the magenta, apricot and flame on the automobiles . . .

There is a sort of Shays' Rebellion going on, we said, in

our overtaxed retinas, and we yearn for utilitarian objects to return to utilitarian colors—drudge grey, spiritless white, mousy taupe and nothing-ever-happens brown.

Apropos, by inversion, of nothing ever happening, Cynthia says her almost legendary Great-aunt Persis, who lives in India and does something about spreading literacy in the villages, is coming to the United States for a visit in the fall.

All right, you mountain lions, I'm *coming*. . . .

February 16th Cora's class mother called this morning and asked if I would come down and help in the school lunchroom. Certain phrases, for me, persist in having a freakish meaning of their own. "Class mother," for example, always gives me a picture of a haughty lady peering through a lorgnette while a British nanny leads her children off to the East Wing. Similarly, the Child Guidance Association—housed in an old Victorian mansion near us—calls up the image of people Cora's age, in white jackets and twirling their eyeglasses, talking kindly and understandingly to sullen, tear-stained, uncooperative adults.

Actually, of course, the class mother sounded harried and democratic. I put on a clean white shirt, piled my hair on top of my head—the rest of me is not pretty, but my hair is—and put on some eye make-up. I keep hearing little arguments about whether women dress for men or for other women, but the most rewarding people to dress for, in reality, are children. Over and over, I hear children say to Friend Cynthia, "Gee, you're pretty!" and they always notice and comment if she has something new or is all dressed up.

Even to me, Cora said admiringly the other day, "You have high cheekbones, don't you?"

Then she added, "You look better than you look."

(The locutions of a nine-year-old are a never-ending source of pleasure. Every morning, getting ready for school, Cora says, "May I take some money of your purse?" and it sounds so medieval that I cannot bring myself to correct her. When we eat in a restaurant and she asks for "kepchup," the waitresses melt.)

Cora did not know I was going to be handing out milk in school, and when she glanced up from the line and saw me, the look of gladsome delight suggested the Donner Party discovering a hot-dog stand.

The pride, faith and trust momentarily contained in that glance first warmed the cockles of my heart and then sobered me and started a serious train of thought.

Why do our children believe in us, if they do?

It is supposed to be our first objective to make them feel "secure"—to shield them from all intrusion of *Sturm und Drang*—but are they more influenced than we realize by how their parents behave in time of crisis? I have thought so, ever since the time during the anti-Communist excitement a few years ago when Harry Fitzgibbons was weighed and not found wanting . . . at least, in his wife's eyes.

Compared with the front-page dramas of the time, it was only a little thing and soon over, but it gave us a horrible insight into what it means to be unpopular when emotions are running high. Harry was asked to testify in behalf of a friend—a former friend, actually—he had not seen the person in some years—who was being given one of the pseudo-lynchings of those days. Harry said he would. And then the phone started ringing; and the burden of everybody's song—friends, acquaintances and relatives—was that Harry should not get tangled up in a *cause célèbre.*

There are only about ten people on the staff where Harry works, although the office is supported from outside by various government authorities, but two of the men from the office came all the way out here one evening to argue—one truculently and one patiently—that Harry should not stick his neck out for someone with whom he was no longer intimate.

Then, too, there was very shortly a feedback from the government authorities about people who impaired their usefulness. Nothing absolutely definite, but the meaning was clear. The government authorities consider Harry a brilliant man with a wonderful record, but of course in those days being brilliant and having a fine record did not save people. We could see ourselves having to sell the house and live on the proceeds.

And when the proceeds were gone? . . .

As to Harry's relatives—once they realized that the wayward kinsman, however beleaguered, would not buy their particular brand of logic—some scathing things were said about the compulsion to martyrdom.

Lord, I shall never forget that period . . . the anguished self-questioning . . . fear like an obscene bird with talons in the vitals . . . the brassy taste in the mouth that defied food, drink and toothpaste.

Nor shall I forget Harry's saying in complete despair, "Doesn't *anybody* understand?"

And then in the end nothing happened.

Harry gave his testimony.

What we had all overlooked was that in those days it was hostile and incriminating evidence that got the billing. Testimony about reliability and good character dropped like a plummet into obscurity. At least, it did if it came from someone who was not famous.

Cora was too young, of course, to know what was going on; but in the years since I have always felt that Harry's parenthood has a kind of ringing tone to it which it would not have if he had taken everyone's advice.

Today was our first spring day. There are many disadvantages to living on a steep hill like ours, but one of the benefits is that when we get a February thaw, it starts literally thousands of little runnels and trickles of water coursing down the slope. I stood on the front path this morning, feeling the warm sun on my cheek, watching the flash and sparkle of all those little rivulets, and hearing their delicious noise . . . I hear that noise once every spring, and I always think of it as A Little Day Music.

While I was fixing dinner this evening, Cora was playing with the cats on the living-room floor. With considerable ingenuity and imagination, she had fixed up a maze— a cat maze, she said—out of old grocery cartons. Old Cat—I knew without having to look—merely sat. Rucked up on his four feet and shoved from behind, he might proceed like furry treacle around two or three corners, but then he would sit again. Young Cat, on the other hand, performed under protest, as a series of indignant "Yahs!" proclaimed, and once he must nearly have made good his escape, for I heard Cora say quietly, "Halt, in the name of me."

February 20th ❧ The Sundays at Seven meeting is almost upon us, and last night Harry and I worked on the talk which, as a member of the panel, I am supposed to give. I think I may have something that will put a little bite into the discussion, but I dunno, I dunno. . . .

It is not that we are a Norman Vincent Peale congregation. On the contrary, Dr. Peale will have to forgive us for looking down on him from dizzying heights of superiority. But for all that, we seem to end up just like the others. It is all love, love, love and it is dull, dull, dull.

Later: ❧ Yesterday after school Cora marked a hem for me. She measured the distance from the floor so carefully and put the pins in so accurately that I had no trouble at all in getting the skirt to look just right. It gave me a pang, though—this momentary translation of my child from one for whom I do things to one who does things for me. The other night, too, she went to bed an hour early— of her own accord, and without any prompting from either parent—because she was completely tired out from ice skating.

When I was a child myself, and a devourer of old-fashioned novels, I always read with complete disbelief the then customary phrase about people having "mingled emotions." It seemed utterly impossible for a person to have more then one feeling at one time. (There wouldn't be *room!*) But these little trajectories of Cora's into competence, rationality and maturity have shown me the last full measure of what we now call "ambivalence"—though I think perhaps the older expression is more descriptive.

I certainly would not want a retarded child, or one neurotically dependent; and I can still remember feeling like a combination of Tom Mooney and the Prisoner of Chillon when Cora was so little that I was pinned to the house for a week if she caught a cold. But when this former urine-soaked-pound-of-flesh goes around pinning up hems like Mainbocher, I get an aching sense of loss about all the manifestations of Cora that are now irretrievably gone.

Oh, well. *Sursum corda.* Lift up the heart. She is still only nine years old. She still says, "Look, Mommy, here's you," and then does an imitation that pulverizes me of her mother talking baby talk to the cats.

And of course, there must be nice things lying ahead.

Her various graduations.

Her first evening dress.

People with older children tell me that once she develops what she now calls "breasters," life will take on a rather continuous quality as of shooting the rapids in a leaky canoe. I do not believe all they say, however — though I am certainly prepared to admit that brains or no brains, Light Horse Harry Fitzgibbons is not going to give up that little girl easily. I can already see him—some years hence—storming up and down our rather diminutive living room and saying, "I don't care if his name *is* Mountbatten, he's still a formless lout!"

Still Later: I am having a cooking binge today, and I have odd bits and segments of time at my disposal while I wait for things to boil, simmer, bake, puff up or cool off. One of the things I have made is a cake for a fund-raising affair at Cora's school—the which I do gladly because of Mrs. Elliott.

We had the usual reason for moving to the suburbs—propinquity to a good public school system—and Cora has never had a really inadequate teacher. (Her parents have paid for this luxury by never having had a really adequate train schedule for getting in and out of the city.) This year, however, Cora has a teacher who is much more than adequate. She is a pedagogical equivalent of the Kohinoor.

The first week of the term, I heard Cora and two other girls in her class agree that Mrs. Elliott was "strick and getting stricker"; and when I went down to visit the class, I discovered Mrs. E. to be a grey-haired lady with a pince-nez who conceals under a sweet manner some of the characteristics associated with the late General Patton. She showed me, on the bulletin board, three or four samples of beautiful penmanship—the best in the class—and said it was her intention to have all the children write equally well by the end of the year.

As hereinbefore noted, Cora's handwriting looks like the track left by an inebriated sparrow, so the avowal of this goal gave me the same feeling of rightness and propriety I would have if Adlai Stevenson were elected President. My daughter's penmanship is not yet up to the standard shown me by Mrs. Elliott, but it is much improved. At the start of the year, Cora's written communications were as inscrutable as the Rosetta Stone, and one had the feeling that could some patient scholar decipher them, they would turn out to be about embalming or reaping the harvest on the delta of the Nile.

Whether because of her age or because of her native character, I do not know, but Mrs. Elliott is sublimely indifferent to the children's "personalities" and is prepared to twist them like pretzels in all the supposedly wrong directions—if by so doing she can enlarge their cranial capacities. She keeps the class late, which infuriates all the tight-schedule mothers. She makes the children do things over. Cora's arithmetic having proved inadequate to the front-line trenches of the intellect she now occupies, Mrs. E. asked Harry and me to drill her night and morning on addition and subtraction.

I did not at all mind making a cake for the Samuel T. Atkinson Grade School, for whenever I drive past it, I feel a happy glow of trust and confidence in thinking of what it shelters within its corrugated, red-tile roof and walls of comfort-station brick. It shelters Cora's fourth-grade teacher—the gentle Spartan, the frilly-bloused scholastic bulldozer, to whom everything in the world is irrelevant saving only pure knowledge and the inculcation of good work habits.

A few days ago Harry brought home from the office— where one of the men had given it to him—a booklet called *Farm Vacations*. This booklet lists working farms that take in boarders and are cheap, and it may prove the solution to how to get away from here for a week next summer.

February 24th ❧ Harry sometimes calls our church St. Euphoria-in-the-Wold, but this name does its architecture, at least, less than justice. The church is classic white New England, with pointed steeple. It dates back so far that it is now in the heart of "downtown" and presides— with its big trees and slanting gravestones—over an area of chop-suey joints, secretarial schools and emporia selling tots' clothing. It really does preside, however, and next to it Commerce—to transpose Shelley's phrase—"shrinks like a thing reproved."

Last night was the Sundays at Seven meeting, and I kept thinking of that severe and classic façade soaring over our heads as I sat with the other panelists at a long deal table in the church basement. Discussion is popular in our meeting house, and about fifty people had turned out.

I was tense.

Tense?

I would have felt more comfortable on a girder fifty floors above the street, catching white-hot rivets in a pail.

Dr. Aspirin chaired the meeting, and in his opening remarks he cued in the "Love thy neighbor" theme; he spoke of the many meanings of the word "love"; he quoted the psychologist, Erich Fromm; he mentioned being unable to love your neighbor unless you could love yourself—i.e., have self-respect; he spoke of constructiveness; he used the word "warmth"; and he implied that the congregation in its labors together (in the Sunday school, and raising money for the parking lot which our location made necessary) was not unfamiliar with the ties that bind.

Dr. Aspirin is not tall, but the beautifully chiseled nose and luminous dark eyes above his brown beard give him a look of distinguished asceticism and passionate theological sincerity. His audience was responsive and admiring. Only one or two faces looked sour.

The sour faces belonged to the old-timers, who were perhaps remembering an era of fifteen years ago, when an earlier pastor of St. Euphoria was trying to get the local bowling alley opened to non-whites. In those not-so-halcyon days, St. Euphoria's repute in the Caucasian part of town was some notches below that of the staphylococcus, and the congregation itself—so Harry and I have been told—was sometimes angrily divided on how far to back up the minister.

Last night, however, that combative and faction-ridden time was one with Nineveh and Tyre.

Dr. Aspirin introduced the panel, which consisted of two other people besides me. One was a middle-aged woman named Myra Smith, who smiled stiffly at the pastor's rather condescending description of her, and whose hands, as she held her little fistful of notes, shook.

The other panelist—to whom the rector did not condescend at all—was a young man from the advertising business, named Tod Everleigh. Tod Everleigh has a ready tongue, nice looks, a pretty wife, two children in the Sunday school, and a house worth $35,000. He is much esteemed, and few people share my feeling that he is glib and that—despite all the appearance of solidity—he really ought to be carrying seeds on the wind.

Everleigh spoke first. Familiarly and half jestingly, he mentioned People's Capitalism, and then talked more seriously about the breaking down of barriers because of the triumph of American production. After that, he took off his economist's hat and put on his psychologist's hat and spoke a little about empathy and the importance of other people in our lives. Like the vicar, he quoted a psychiatrist—in this case, Harry Stack Sullivan.

With a final flourish of documentation, he turned to religion and read something from a book of Reinhold Niebuhr's—after which he relaxed to the secular arm and told some charming little illustrative stories about family life and some amusing anecdotes about the mildly celebrated ($80,000,000 a year billing) firm for which he works.

Oddly enough, I was haunted all during the talk by a sense of the *déjà vu*—of something evoked from the past —although what young Everleigh said was as modern as a photoelectric eye. Just as he finished, I pinned it down. I remembered reading somewhere that the Virginia novelist, Ellen Glasgow, was once asked what the South needed most.

"Blood and irony," she said.

However, in being reminded of Miss Glasgow's tart diagnosis, I was listening to the music of a different drummer, for it seemed to be the feeling of the meeting that—with Everleigh's contribution added to Dr. Aspirin's—the evening was made.

Poor Myra Smith was the next speaker. A miserably strained and self-conscious performer, she gave a talk that, clearly, nobody had helped her with. It was all Victorian sentiment about kind hearts and coronets. But its florid periods were soon over, and Dr. Aspirin was introducing me. (How? In what vein? I did not hear. I was too busy clearing my throat.)

I began my talk by mentioning that the philosophers say a thing exists in terms of its opposite. So—I said—I thought I would discuss love in terms of hate.

The Canterbury pilgrims in front of me straightened up, but now that I was into the thing, I had miraculously lost my nervousness and I plunged straight ahead.

I spoke of the cleansing quality of hate and anger—referred to the Augean stables and the money-changers driven out of the temple—raised the question of intensity and asked whether it is possible to have a capacity for love without an equal capacity for indignation.

42

Wasn't there, I asked, a distinction to be made between love and mere permissiveness—love being what you feel about a person for whom you will fight and get really embroiled?

Having with some embroidery and illustration raised these issues—it was, after all, supposed to be a discussion group—I sat down; but the little spatter of automatic and good-natured applause which had rewarded the other speakers did not materialize. There was total silence. A number of people looked hopefully at Dr. Aspirin, but all that was visible of him was the delicate profile as he stroked one of the hands in his lap.

Then Harry—wonderful man!—slewed round in his front-row seat and looked at everybody, turned up his coat collar, gave a shiver, and said, "Whew! The wind, she blow on Lac St. Pierre."

Everybody laughed, and the tension relaxed.

It was by no means, however, wholly dissolved.

Dr. Aspirin said slowly that perhaps I meant we should hate the sin, but love the sinner.

Before I could answer, one of the old-timers—not waiting to be recognized by the chair—said, "That's nice work if you can get it. But can anyone seriously imagine hating Hitler's sin, but loving Hitler?"

A middle-aged lady raised her hand urgently, got the nod of recognition, and told a long story about how her sister had been sent a wild young rebel from a city newspaper's Fresh Air Fund and had turned him into a junior Ralph Bunche in a mere two weeks of unmitigated affection.

On several of the more intelligent faces I could see the almost visible thought that the youngster, in that case, must have been completely ruined for the slum life he had to go back to. But before anything confusing or ambivalent could be said, Tod Everleigh casually signaled Dr. Aspirin for permission to speak. Then, with a reassuring smile and an air of negligent command, he adduced St. Francis of Assisi and Gandhi as conclusive proof that people can love without hating or getting angry.

My co-religionists sighed happily.

"But," I protested, with some heat, "Gandhi and St. Francis were professionals when it came to the milk of human kindness. They worked at it full-time. They lived on the subsistence level so they could."

Eyes opened a little wider. Spines straightened. Devoted as my audience was to loving the neighbor, I had a feeling they were preparing to make an exception in my case.

Nevertheless, I persisted.

"I don't see how we here in the suburbs, with our dishwashers and station wagons and all our comforts, can compare ourselves with Gandhi and St. Francis."

To my surprise I observed, from certain stiffenings of displeasure here and there, that that was what some of them *had* been comparing themselves to—at least on the score of not hating.

However, by this time Dr. Aspirin had things under control again.

"We have an answer nearer home," he said. "The bus boycott in Montgomery, Alabama. Dr. Martin Luther King told his parishioners over and over again not to hate the white people."

"That wasn't love—that was just a relaxed sell," said a voice from the back of the room. A slightly mocking voice.

There was a little spurt of laughter from a few people, but others did not laugh.

Harry jumped in quickly.

"The Negroes in Montgomery were using a weapon," he said. "At least, the bus company thought so."

But by now hands were up all over the room, and as Dr. Aspirin permitted first one and then another to speak, the occasion was deluged with stories on the love-conquers-all theme.

The inevitable suburban lady spoke about children and arrived at the inevitable gay and cheery conclusion that "All you have to do is love them."

Another woman said she had had from childhood a test of whether she loved even hateful people, like Hitler or Senator McCarthy. Her test was to imagine she saw them about to be run over by a truck and to ask herself whether she would save them. She always found she would. To date, the wheels of that phantasmal vehicle were innocent of blood.

I began to realize (I thought) what Dr. Aspirin was doing. He was, in his role of chairman, giving the preference to the sentimentalists. But when I took a second look, I saw that I had done the dominie an injustice. He was not ignoring the intelligent people. The intelligent people did not have their hands up. They were sitting this one out.

I had just made this appalling discovery when a curly-headed, bespectacled young woman jumped to her feet with one of those utterly hopeless garblings of the issue that make parliamentary democracy so taxing to the nervous system.

"I'd like to ask the panel," said the young lady waspishly, "I'd like to ask Mrs. Fitzgibbons . . . what about juvenile delinquents? They're full of hate and anger; does she admire them?"

Panel and audience alike looked a little daunted at the prospect of untangling this plate of mental spaghetti.

But suddenly an interruption occurred.

An unexpected supporter rallied to my side of the argument. Ignoring Curlyhead—who waited a minute and then plumped huffishly down—poor, squeaky, stammering Myra Smith said she thought she understood what I was getting at.

The Bible, Myra said, tells us to love our enemies, our own enemies. But what about loving other people's enemies? Should Christians love the Nazis who killed six million Jews? Should liberals love the people in the White Citizens' Councils?

Dr. Aspirin's face wore the expression of one who has a soufflé in the oven when they start blasting down the street.

But a cranky old man who has long admired the vicar rose impetuously and said in arbitrary tones that we cannot transcend our limitations as individuals and that we must often deplore and disapprove of things we are helpless to change.

This politic statement got almost the same pleased reception as the discovery of gold in Sutter's Creek, and Chairman Aspirin took advantage of the general relaxation to announce that our time was up and to bring the meeting to a close.

The rector is punctilious in his manners, and as people began to mill about, he went to the refreshment table and came back with coffee for Mrs. Smith and me. But I was too full of emotion to taper off readily into commonplaces, and when he started to thank us for our contribution to the evening, I said, " 'Thou hast conquered, O pale Galilean.' "

I guess the evening was not a total loss.

Evidently, the Abbé Aspirin once read Swinburne, too.

His face above the brown beard was a study.

February 27 〜 I find myself, when I think of it, having a feeling of pleasurable anticipation about meeting Cynthia's Great-aunt Persis in the fall. Not entirely because she is a distinguished woman (as opposed to a mere celebrity), but because she suggests horizons.

Great-aunt Persis springs—I learn from Cynthia—from the famous moral avant-garde of which Mrs. Roosevelt is the dominant figure; and back in the days when Mrs. Roosevelt started inviting Negroes to the White House, Great-aunt Persis took up those cudgels, too. Since she had through her social work a wide acquaintance with law-enforcement bodies, she became largely instrumental in getting municipal police departments opened to Negroes, and I seldom see a Negro policeman nowadays without thinking of Great-aunt Persis—and of the many years when all policemen were white and everyone took it for granted.

But Cynthia's great-aunt has been in India now, confronting the illiteracy problem, for some ten or twelve years, and she is probably at home there, for she started out as a child of Asia. Orphaned at an early age, she was brought up by an aunt and uncle who were in the export business in China. She speaks Chinese, and was the friend of all three of the famous Soong sisters—which rather suggests some kind of socio-political Auntie Mame.

I cannot help but feel in awe at the breadth and scope of that experience. To be casually at ease, so to speak, on a continent the size of Asia! Not to mention having a record of pioneering social achievement in the United States. It makes me feel exceedingly suburban and limited, and I have to cling a little tighter than usual to the wonderful, sonorous, echoing line of Milton's—"They also serve who only stand and wait."

March 2nd ❧ Harry and I looked over the *Farm Vacations* booklet last night. The price of hospitality at these agricultural establishments is wonderfully modest, but we do not know what this means. What do you not get, for the money you do not pay? All the descriptions of the manors, freeholds and homesteads sound like something out of Virgil's *Georgics*—swimming, good food, beautiful countryside.

"How," I said to Harry, "in this box of pastoral chocolates, are we going to find the nougat and avoid the candied fig?"

I have a vague recollection of having been taken to spend a couple of weeks on a third cousin's farm when I was very small, and Harry went to a boys' camp which was run in conjunction with a farm. We also saw a picture with Jeanne Crain called *State Fair,* and I remember murmuring to Harry—as the camera moved from crisply chintzy kitchen to well-appointed cow barn—"They should have called it *The Vision of Piers Plowman.*"

But farm life is terra incognita for us. After much deliberation, we picked out a dairy farm about four hundred miles away and wrote to ask whether they can put us up for the second week in July.

"It's like going to the Balkans," I said to Harry as I

pressed a stamp down on the letter. "I can't form any pictures in my mind."

"I can't form any pictures," he said, "that are consistent with thirty-dollar-a-week board. But after all, we aren't committed to it."

March 6th ❧ I have just been for a long walk, to inspect for signs of spring the few pocket-handkerchiefs of woodland that are left us by the influx of population. I return home dissatisfied with the convention which dictates that the lily shall be the emblem of purity. At noontime of a March day—with skies a newly minted blue, and a high wind pouring across the planet—white houses and white birches have a stainless radiance compared to which Madonna lilies are as used paper napkins.

In front of the Samuel T. Atkinson Grade School, the wind had set the American flag to snapping like a husky at feeding time, and since it was lunch hour, kites bucked and plunged overhead. Not, in most cases, very far overhead. I cannot come home from viewing Nature in such ebullient mood and do the ironing. It is too menial. So I will make a pot of tea, to warm myself up, and read. (Speaking of purity, incidentally, why is a harmless and innocuous plant burdened with a name like "skunk cabbage," while the organism which leaves empty beer cans on every lot not actually occupied enjoys the title of "Homo sapiens"?)

I can spare a little time to read this afternoon, because Harry is working late and will not be home to dinner. As I once remarked to him, there is only one thing wrong with Harry's monthly salary check—pernicious anemia.

Furthermore, a regional planner comes up oftener than most people against the all-too-human attitude—carefully rationalized, but unmistakable—of *"I'm* comfortable, so why should I care about anyone else?" (I suspect, as a matter of fact, that it is his frequent and not always successful collisions with entrenched greed that make H. Fitzgibbons so inveterately mocking.)

But we have in our town branches of two internationally famous corporations, and they have taught me not to resent the so-called limitations of Harry's job. These corporations are enamored of the word "family," when it comes to describing their personnel; and within their Vitaglass precincts, nobody collides with anything. It is all coffee breaks, bull sessions and blamelessness. (I have my operatives in there, so I know.) They pay generous salaries, but working for one of those giant corporations is like sitting down to eat two quarts of white sauce. It will keep body and soul together, but who wants it?

And speaking of body and soul, Harry is walking with a cane these days. The cane is borrowed (where else?) from one of the stuffy uncles who urged him not to testify for his friend (and I think now, from the hearty solicitousness with which he pressed the cane on us, is a little ashamed of that craven counsel). What necessitated the cane was the fact of Young Cat scampering among Harry's ankles at a moment when Harry happened to be walking among them himself.

Tuan Fitzgibbons—ever the upper-class chappie with the interests of the weak and helpless foremost in his mind —tried not to hurt the cat. With this laudable and chivalrous intent, he took both feet off the ground at once and measured his length heavily on the carpet. It was a mag-

nificant parabola, and brought instantly to mind the
poet's line—

"From morn
To noon he fell, from noon to dewy eve."

However—as I tried to explain later—what made me
laugh was not a banana-peel sense of humor, but merely a
slight form of hysteria because I know that cat-and-foot
sensation so well. One feels so *weighty*—like the statue of
the Commandant in *Don Giovanni*. It is only a trifle worse
than the intimation—a split second before the horren-
dous screech—that what one's heavily shod foot is irretrievably descending on is the cat's tail.

Young Cat compounded the injury by leaning over from
the bookcase top—where he was acting like Maria Callas
about his ruffled fur—and saying, "Nnnnnyeeeeeaaah!"
in a tone compounding scorn, outrage and rank ingrati-
tude. What Harry, from the floor, said to Young Cat was
presumably derived from that fountainhead of elegance,
the Merchant Marine.

Anyway, in a surprisingly short time Harry had a
honeydew melon where his ankle used to be, and the doctor had to come over and minister to it. Our doctor is not
overwhelmingly popular in neurasthenic circles because
—short, bald, mustached and taciturn—he has the impassivity of a clinical thermometer and is therefore a hard
audience to dramatize yourself for. But Harry and I have
had a muted rapprochement with him which dates from
the day I said to his nurse, "My husband isn't feeling well.
I think he must have gotten some socialized medicine."

One reason we like Dr. Potter is that he does not instantly drench the ailing protoplasm with tranquilizers and miracle drugs. He prefers to let people toss and moan a bit while he finds out what is really the matter. Harry and I find this reassuring, as we are a little nervous about the headlong miracles of modern medicine. We can never quite get over a fear that some slam-bang chemical which is going to knock out the Black Death in half an hour will also turn out—through being rushed into production too fast—to produce a banner crop of warts or make us grow two heads.

At any rate, Dr. Potter came and twinkled his eyeglasses at us, and Harry will be all right again soon—although the first morning he went to the office and I found him standing in the front hall hatted, gloved and leaning on the cane, I said, "Where are you bound for, Planner? Lourdes?"

March 9th ❧ We had a letter from the farm the day before yesterday, saying they can put us up for the second week in July, and enclosing two snapshots. One is of an old-fashioned, nineteenth-century house with cupola. It is standing half surrounded by a grove of trees, but the picture is taken from so far away—in order to get all of the house in, apparently—that no details can be seen. The other picture is of the mother and father and four children. The mother is wearing a housedress. The rest are in jeans. Everything is blurred, but they all seem windblown and smiling. The children range in age from twelve to twenty-one. My correspondent gave names and ages in her letter. The names are fancy—Vanessa and

Rayleine for the girls, Fanshawe and Henderson for the boys.

The letter is signed "Miriam Brown" and has a sort of cheery, self-respecting quality about it. Mrs. Brown asks if we have any snapshots, and if we can tell them a little about ourselves. She also says to bring old clothes, and a few warm sweaters, as it often gets chilly in the evening. I had asked when I originally wrote whether there would be anything to keep Cora amused, and Mrs. Brown says they never have any trouble keeping the children occupied.

It is absurd, but my mind keeps forming the most idyllic pictures of peace and plenty—scrubbed pantries with bowls of cream and strawberries and a smell of homemade cake, a garden of old-fashioned flowers like delphinium and verbena and sweet william, even a privy with honeysuckle and an untended Dorothy Perkins rose twining over it and the hot sun beating down and a sound of bees. I am old enough to know that life just isn't like that, and that these ideas are resurrections from forgotten novels about the English countryside; but much as I try to think myself into an Erskine Caldwell vein, the fantasies persist.

March 10th ❧ Friend Cynthia and the boys—the beautiful one and the stubborn one—stopped in this morning, and we ladies drank coffee and had what conversation we could while the Brothers Karamazov held shooting affrays and cut each other off at the pass. Save for the fact that I recognize someone must bring up a handsome and intel-

❧53

ligent male for Cora to marry, I would be a little impatient with boys.

"It will be a great thing," I think to myself—observing the creatures with what might be charitably described as detachment—"when all that energy is going into procreation and/or writing the Ring Cycle. But in the meantime, haven't we all, perhaps, been a little too critical of eunuchs?"

However, I do love Cynthia, and she loves the boys, so I love them at secondhand. I asked Cynthia if she had seen Lippmann's column this morning—which was a stupid question, as she was up by five o'clock at her easel—and she sighed and said absent-mindedly, "I guess Walter Lippmann is all right, but don't you think the supply is just a little bigger than the demand?"

My beautiful neighbor had disappointing news. Great-aunt Persis is not, after all, going to be staying out here with Cynthia and Russell when she comes to the U.S. in the fall. Originally, her trip was planned merely as a holiday and to visit relatives, for she is seventy years old and will no doubt die in harness. But gradually the expedition has come to be almost completely professional. Great-aunt Persis will be raising money for Reading-for-India and having discussions with UNESCO people, with foundations, with the government and with educators. She has also promised to fly to Canada and the Middle West to give speeches.

"Water seeks its own level," Cynthia said reasonably, but we are both disappointed. We had looked forward to being in intimate touch with somebody who is doing something immediately and every day to change the shape of the world. Not that either Cynthia or I incline to look on our own roles with contempt; but Great-aunt Persis has been stirring up the yeast which is causing whole land masses to ferment, and we had looked forward to bringing her cups of tea and hassocks for her feet and hearing about subcontinents until the wee small hours.

However, one must ride with the punches, as the Male Animals say, and Great-aunt Persis will come out to Cynthia's for dinner and to stay overnight.

March 11th I went in to the great city this morning to have lunch with Harry and be accompanied by him while I shopped for a new dress. On those occasions when I count my blessings and they stay counted—because sometimes you can count them but they refuse to register —one of the leading blessings is Harry's good taste and self-confident judgment about women's clothes.

My difficulty in selecting wearing apparel is that I am a starved romantic at heart. I long for floating chiffon scarves and exquisite ruffles of mousseline de soie, but knowing I am just not the type for these felicities, I tend to overcompensate and buy something like the dark-green knit.

When Harry first saw the dark-green knit, he said politely, "Dear me! Are you studying for the ministry?"

Today, however, we found a silk print which, worn with very high heels and my hair in a French roll, makes me look properly carnal and as if I had my mind on lower things. The whole excursion was so delightfully companionable that I found myself thinking, for the first time in years, about people who are unmarried. If you are raising children in the suburbs, there are two things you never see—

(1) a spinster of this parish
(2) a bachelor

I was a spinster once, and Harry was a bachelor, but the current seems to have borne us so swiftly away from the giddy vicissitudes of mate-selection that the unmarried are now almost a strange race. Of course, we will get reintroduced to them when Cora grows up. Or will we? From what one hears, the new generation starts "going steady" at the age of twelve, and considers the single blessedness of a Dag Hammarskjold or an E. M. Forster quite insupportable.

March 14th ❧

> "Spring rides no horses down the hill,
> But comes on foot, a goose girl still."

Miss Millay was probably not thinking of it at the time, but she could scarcely have found a better way of saying that March is the month of the Girl Scout cookie drive. I warm to the goose-girl simile, for I am cookie chairman of Cora's Brownie troop . . . and the title of cookie chairman certainly suggests the barefoot herdswoman rather more than Madame Ambassador.

This is my second year as cookie chairman and I have now learned to take it in stride. Last year, however, both the Brownies and I were new at the job, and my efforts to collate the outflow of cookies with the inflow of money bordered on the frantic.

Last year, for some reason—I suppose because the Girl Scouts wear uniforms, and I am the stuff of which conscientious objectors are made—I was haunted by a pervasive nightmare of Prussian militarism. I could see myself being short of the required sum when the cookie drive was over. I could see the drumhead court-martial and the stern-faced women in field green. I could see the little back room where they left me with a revolver and a bottle of brandy. I could see the Girl Scout Council tapping their riding crops on the table and waiting to hear the shot which would heal the wounded honor of Troop 50, Neighborhood 6.

Actually, of course, there was not much about the enterprise to suggest the late Erich von Stroheim. On an appointed day, I waited in until some truckmen brought thirty-five cartons of cookies and left them in the middle of the living-room floor. It was a mountain of cardboard and only a supply sergeant could have thrilled to it. Then I went out to get something for dinner. When I returned, I found Cora and some friends had come in and they were playing a game for which thirty-five cartons of cookies are the well-nigh perfect equipment. The game was called Run-for-your-lives-the-dam-has-broken.

To this day, I flinch at the memory. How many people in this community bought Girl Scout cookies—thinking the wafers would be circular and the sandwich crackers *virgo intacta*—and found they had purchased merely a sort of perishable gravel?

Nevertheless, I have a soft spot in my heart for the Girl Scouts because I was one myself. I can still remember that for some amount which seems utterly paltry now—something like $10 or $7 or $12 a week—my parents sent me to Scout camp and introduced me to an experience whose glory has not wholly faded, even yet. I can still recall the gorgeous novelty of tent life, the Spenserian magic of the woods by moonlight, the coziness when a downpour drummed on the canvas and the flaps were shut. (Who cared if it was a little stuffy?) I can still recollect the triumph, not quite to be believed, of having learned to swim. And the Jack London, *coureur-de-bois* flavor of the overnight pack trip abideth even yet.

Those memories came back vividly on the day last year when Cora first wore her Brownie uniform. She stood in the hall waiting to show herself to Harry—a small, cocoa-colored shape against the white banisters, her hair in pigtails to accommodate the Brownie skullcap and her face so luminous with innocent pride that it was like a candle burning in a windless place. When Harry opened the door and came in, she saluted. He looked down at her.

Parental tenderness occasionally overwhelms.

The great, gruff regional planner with the lean-flanked intellect and the satiric wit had the hackneyed old "suspicion of moisture" in his eyes. And I myself had a lump in my throat like a croquet ball.

Thus do the unwary fall into cookie chairmanships.

March 18th ❧ Everybody else's crocuses are up, but not mine, not mine!

March 25th ❧ Cora raised a question at the breakfast table this morning which her percipient and knowledgeable elders had not thought of. What are we going to do about Young Cat and Old Cat when we go to the farm in July?

We can, of course, leave them at the vet's, if the worst

comes to the worst, but they come back smelling of disinfectant and they punish us by a haughty withdrawal from conversation and embraces. After one weekend, in fact, when we had consigned them to that Avernus of cages and barking dogs, Young Cat went through the house in vengeful fury and nipped off every single one of the little round circles that terminate the window-shade pulls.

The ideal solution would be to find some reliable adolescent—I refuse to use that boring and repellant word "teen-ager"—who would come in and take care of them. Preferably someone tenderhearted, who would not only feed them and change their pans, but also listen to Young Cat's Ciceronian orations and give Old Cat at least a small fraction of the lavish personal contact he can never get enough of.

We sometimes refer to Old Cat as the G.I. member of the family. G.I. stands not for Government Issue but for Greed Incarnate, and it is a greed for food and for demonstrations of affection in about equal parts. Old Cat wants to lie down next to whoever is sleeping, curl up in the lap of whoever is sitting, and crawl up on the shoulder of, and breathe ticklishly into the ear of, whoever is typing, totting up expenses or doing anything else which is not noticeably expedited by a fur neckpiece weighing ten pounds. Once established in any of these havens, Old Cat begins and maintains a stertorous purring that sounds like an avalanche rumbling in the middle distance but never getting any nearer.

When I set it down in cold type, I begin to feel with some embarrassment that we are fools to put up with these cats. All the food in our house, for instance—unless it is on a plate on the dining-room table with a human being hunched protectively over it—has to be shut up in a cupboard or put away on a high shelf. Young Cat is relatively ascetic. He filches only meat and fish. But Old Cat will eat *anything*—string beans, asparagus, bread, butter. . . . We have sometimes even wondered whether he has been at the vitamin pills.

One evening last summer Harry ate half a canteloupe before going to sleep and left the rind on top of the bookcase in our bedroom. We usually—digging them out from under the blankets on Cora's bed—shut the cats in the kitchen the last thing before we go to sleep, for they like to spend the silent watches sharpening their claws on the living-room furniture. But that night we must have forgotten. Or perhaps they got out. At any rate, some time in the witching hours Old Cat—who has a veritably Persian lust for melon—managed to convey that unwieldy piece of refuse in his neat little triangle of jaw all the way down to the kitchen. (What a Rake's Progress it must have been! I should like to have seen it.)

Once considerably established on the linoleum, he chewed up and spat out the entire rind, in quarter-inch pieces, and distributed them with a fine impartiality up and down and across the entire floor. When Harry and I came down in the morning, we could only stare in silence —not so much angry at the mess as awed by the size of the accomplishment.

"Gosh!" said Harry in a small voice. "He must have been sired by a Dispose-all."

March 26th 〰 Everyone is agreed that the uniformity and stifling comfort of the suburbs are bad; but the suburbs do provide a sense of the changing seasons and the revolving year that is hard to come by in the city. In the same intensity, that is. Every spring, the day we open the porch is a glorious beginning; and every fall, the day we close up the porch is a terminus—a little melancholy, but not without promise of shelter and intimacy.

Of course, we are six weeks away from opening up the porch, but today was a Saturday and Harry and I dragged the porch furniture out on the lawn and painted it pussy-willow grey. As a general thing, to be sure, we Fitz-gibbonses eschew the application of pigment to the surfaces among which we live; but even we would not go so far as to hire someone to paint the porch furniture.

And today we were happy in our task.

Although the brown ravages of winter are still everywhere in evidence, it was one of those days of early spring when five senses seem like almost too many, so unbearably promising is the warm sun, so heady the discovery of little leaf buds on the bush honeysuckle. Even the mud smells good; and across the street—where the occupants are devout and successful gardeners—a bank of royal blue scillas burns sacramentally, like a fragment of stained glass that has somehow gotten loose from Chartres.

"Dorothy Canfield Fisher," I said to Harry, laying down my paintbrush, "had a good phrase somewhere about 'the useful bodies of the middle-aged,' and I try to keep it in mind."

I took off my rubber gloves and pushed my hair back with both hands, so that the sun could get at every last pore in my face.

"But on days like this, I can't help feeling that a great courtesan was lost in me."

Harry smiled mischievously.

61

"I know what you mean," he said. "It's love-potion weather. Very adulterous and Tristany."

But by half past three—quarter of four at the latest—the winter chill has come back; and one is glad to go indoors and think of tea and a piece of cake, instead of philters. It is amazing, though, how long the skin of the cheek stays cool from the last somewhat-too-prolonged half hour of trying to get the painting finished.

April 2nd ❧ When I was a young person and had to memorize the celebrated passage beginning "Sweet are the uses of adversity," I did not quite know what it meant. Sermons in trees? Books in the running brooks? Now, however, a more vivid example comes instantly to mind. If I had the kind of food budget which permitted unlimited expenditures at the Quelques Choses à Manger, I should soon reach dimensions that required my being lodged in one of those hangars at Lakehurst. The Quelques Choses à Manger sells food delicacies—brioches, canapés, desserts, beef burgundy—and, as might be expected, it is rather more the rendezvous of chauffeur-driven Cadillacs than of two-wheeled carts drawn by burros.

I was in there with Harry one day when a lady of uncramped means casually ordered about thirty dollars' worth of tarts, tortes and other improvements on unleavened bread; and I guess my face must have showed rather transparently a certain amount of greed and envy, because when we got outside again into the plain, unfragrant air, Harry said, "Actually, if you could buy their stuff all the time, it would be as commonplace as a piece of toast."

I know.

I can see him now, that fellow who comes home on the 4:53 Bankers' Special. He sits at the head of the refectory table in his Citizen Kane dining room. His lips are taut. His foot taps. His nostrils flare.

"Pâté de fois gras and flaky French pastry *again!*" he is saying bitterly to himself. "Why can't she fry me some grease-splattered eggs?"

April 10th 〜 Friend Cynthia called up this afternoon to report without undue elation that there is a rather long piece about Great-aunt Persis and Reading-for-India in the current issue of *Time.* An acquaintance down the street had phoned and told her about it. One of the things Cynthia and I have in common is a dislike of *Time,* which we both think is smart-alecky, know-it-all and condescending to its betters.

"There's nothing wrong with *Time* that a crown of thorns wouldn't cure," a man in Harry's office once said.

This critical feeling, however, is not shared by Cynthia's neighbors. They called her up—several of them—in a state of animation and excitement about the accolade and laughingly used the phrase "reflected glory." Cynthia found herself unable to match their enthusiasm, and was depressed by the whole thing.

"You must learn to live with it," I said to her firmly. "In these parts, *Time* has Newspapal Infallibility."

I called Harry at the office and asked him to bring home

a copy, and we were glad to see that Great-aunt Persis was treated with a proper respect—no doubt because of sharing with the proprietor the advantages of a Chinese background.

Oddly enough, in spite of the magazine's highly touted reputation for clarity, I often find *Time*'s prose reminiscent of tangled wire coathangers. I recall they once used "the magniloquence of maudlin" to describe an actor's performance, and just try to unhook *that* in a hurry! And in this issue there is a sentence describing a movie as "a poignant restatement of the timeless truth that a social problem is a moral problem, which can only have a religious solution."

But even with *Time*'s ambiguities, what got across about Great-aunt Persis was the unswerving generosity and the absence of pettiness.

"It's a good thing she wasn't here during the McCarthy period," I could not help thinking. "She's just the kind of person they went after."

Time ran a picture of Cynthia's great-aunt, and I had to revise my preconceived notion of her. I had imagined her as small, stocky and spunky; but she is the Edwardian lady—still dark-haired and looking tall, radiant and commanding even against an amorphous but definitely nonsensual background that seemed to be a village in India.

April 12th ⤙ Every year the mild exigents of the P.T.A. set Harry to mumbling that there was not, after all, anything so very terrible about Dotheboys Hall.

Not for parents, anyway.

We feel, as everybody does, that we really ought to do our bit in the P.T.A.; but we contemplate this obligation with all the infectious zest the Air Force has for infantry warfare.

The first few years we made strenuous and unblushing efforts to get assigned to something really minimal—like the Ad Hoc Committee for Fishing Small Babies Out of Manholes or the Special Advisory Board for Publicizing the Gerund. But last year and again this year we got sandbagged—both of us—onto the Program Committee; and here we must cope with the fact that the local reproducers of their kind do not want to come out in the evening except for a "name," and anyone who counts as a "name" on these Parnassian slopes usually gets $500 just for clearing his throat.

Harry has dragged in every urban renewer and Portly Authority—to use Cora's term—he could lay his hands on. Another man on the committee—who is in personnel work—has ensnared all the psychological testers between here and the Aberdeen Proving Grounds. But now we have shot our bolt. The cupboard is bare. We are seriously considering opening next year's program with the man who runs the meat department at Plethora, Inc.

The Program Committee does, however, give Harry and me an idea of our "status" in these parts. The members of the committee refer to Harry with affectionate raillery as an intellectual giant. As for me, the male members of the committee are not aware of my existence, but to the female members I am a sort of "clean" Vincent van Gogh. Nobody entertains any serious apprehensions about my cutting off an ear; but the floors in my house are scuffed, stained and innocent of wax (they have carpets only in the center, and not always there) and I will tolerate anything on them except prostrate drunks. If that is not the sign of a mad genius, what is?

Harry and I are aware that when we meet with the Program Committee—knee to knee in the midst of somebody's department-store Chippendale—the little flags that say "All right" do not go up in their brains. Nevertheless, the committee members do sometimes (to quote one of them) get a bounce out of our wacky ideas—and last night there occurred one such marriage of true minds.

When the discussion had faltered to its unsatisfactory conclusions and we were all drinking coffee before leaving, one of the men remarked with awe in his voice that his older boy had been at work in the cellar till one o'clock the night before on a thrustomometer. The purpose of the thrustomometer is to measure the impetus needed by a small rocket that the high-school science class is making under government supervision.

"Gosh," said the man ruefully. "These kids know so much more than we do."

"About what?" I asked. "Roberts' Rules of Order? How to write the familiar essay? What George Washington meant by his concept of 'honor'?"

Interested faces turned toward me.

"I'm getting pretty fed up with science," I said, "and I refuse to be daunted any more by the Green Pasteurs of the local high school."

There was a startled, involuntary laugh.

"What are the young people doing," I asked, "in *political* science?"

I put down my coffee cup.

"These youngsters don't know more than we do. They may even know less, because when we went to school, the discipline was stricter and the schools weren't so crowded."

"Hear! Hear!" said the personnel man, and somebody clapped.

"As for rockets," I added, "I don't even give them the time of day.

"Space is a fine and private place,
But none, I think, do there embrace."

No comment was made, but a certain brightening of interest and a clear receptivity were distinctly in evidence; and when Harry helped me into the car on the way home, he said, "Look at you awready! An emancipator yet."

"That's me," I replied smugly. "The Simon Bolivar of the P.T.A."

April 15th ❦ Today was the first spring storm—the first inclemency that was unmistakably of the summer and not of the winter. It had been a lovely morning, but around eleven o'clock the sunlight dimmed and then disappeared, and in the northwest (a good strong quarter of the sky and one of my favorites) a dark cloud materialized and in no time at all spread to the zenith. A slate-colored cloud, it seemed almost navy blue because of all the golden forsythia and daffodil beneath it.

Then came the wind, up-ending dead leaves and swirling the dust, and it was a warm wind—the warmest the winter-weary skin had felt since Michaelmas. The rain came in big drops, and since I was watching this tempest from the garage—whither I had gone to empty trash—I was able to stick out an arm and take the temperature of the downpour, and that was warm, too. But the real signs of the new season were the transverse of lightning which slashed across the navy blue and the clumsy sound of thunder that, after a moment, confirmed it. The dark and battered hulk of winter had been cut loose, and the year was light and free and unencumbered again.

Standing in the garage door with the fledgling summer, I had the best and the worst of the suburbs contiguous to each other, as it were; for the garage looks out over the shoulder of the hill to the flatlands below and there, flung across the landscape like a plucked chicken on the kitchen table, is the development. The structures that make up the development are known in our family as Tinkelpaugh houses.

The lyric adjective evolved from a chance remark.

A couple of streets away, Harry and I used to have a favorite stretch of five or six grassy, beautiful, unoccupied lots which boasted some noble hemlocks. About two years ago, however, the owner of the lots sold them to an entrepreneur who was drunk with power saws. This gentleman cut down the trees and put up a row of five or six little houses in a design that has grown all too painfully familiar. The houses have the well-known boxy outline, the inevitable picture window, and the chimney which does not mature into a fireplace but goes straight up like a square drinking straw.

Mournfully contemplating these dish-faced and featureless façades, I said to Harry, "You expect the whole front to swing down on hinges. And inside will be a loaf of Grandma Tinkelpaugh's Saltee Rye, in a red-white-and-blue wrapping."

Since then Tinkelpaugh houses have taken their place

in our vocabulary on an equal footing with Doric capitals and Perpendicular cathedrals. It is at least something to have a name for them.

April 17th 〰 I usually look through the local paper with a jaundiced eye, for it is on the opposite side of the fence from me politically, and I glance at it mostly to see what the prisoners of error are up to and whether they have accidentally stumbled on anything which honesty compels me to admit is right. They never have, and honesty never does—which is what I like about honesty. I did notice tonight, however, that they had a little squib saying Great-aunt Persis would be visiting Cynthia for several weeks in the fall—a bit of information apparently culled from the time when the original plans were still in force.

April 20th 〰 Cora, shimmering pinkly like a Renoir, has gone off to a birthday-party-supper at a friend's house; and although I smile at the recollection of the shining pony tail, arched like the handle on a very large teacup, the name of the French painter does not have uniformly pleasant associations in my mind. This is not because of anything pertaining to painting. It is because—thanks to television and mass culture—"Renn-wahr" is the way my daughter and her friends pronounce "running water."

For my part, my only criticism of the 100,000 (is it?) words in the English language is that there are not enough of them. I could use more. Failing that, I like to give each syllable of my native tongue its full value. But I am living with a rising generation which talks like people coming out of ether.

"Use your lips!" I say to Cora. "Use your teeth! Use your tongue!"

I have a list thumbtacked to the window casement over the kitchen sink, and every time Cora says "bewdyful" for "beautiful" or pronounces "dance" or "Francis" as if she were whinnying for a bag of oats, I write down the offending locution. Since she is already doing arithmetic drill night and morning for Mrs. Elliott (and what an intellectual Danse Macabre, after a placid beginning, *that* turned out to be!) I have made an agreement to help her with the breakfast dishes if she will practice doing the list correctly. She is amiable and obliging. She goes through the words several times, working up eventually to a rendition that would be a credit to Eleanora Duse. Then she turns away and says, "Wuh-wuh-wuh-wuh-wuh-muh-lunch?"

Last week, however, I made an interesting sort of educational discovery—what the Germans call *Heimatkunst,* I suppose. I usually only half listen to Cora when she speaks to me. Often I think I know what she is going to say. Often I am wondering whether I can get croquettes out of what is left of the ham, or perhaps trying to remember the words of some long-forgotten song like "Mother's in the Baggage Car Ahead."

But last week—with no very well-formulated idea in mind, just some vague notion of trying another tack—I started putting everything else out of my head when she spoke to me and giving what she said my full attention. It was difficult at first, but I got the knack of it after a while. To my delight, the attentive glance and completely receptive ear seem to be doing what all my desperate admonitions failed to do. She is beginning to speak better.

April 24th ✒ I dropped in at Cynthia's this afternoon to return to some unsweetened chocolate I had borrowed, and she said, "Stay awhile. Mrs. Brock Chancellor is coming to tea. She wants to see me."

I raised my eyebrows in surprise.

"What about?" I asked.

Mrs. Brock Chancellor works for just about everything that Cynthia and I think is worth working for, from planned parenthood and better education for the disadvantaged to urban renewal and nuclear disarmament. When delegations go to the state capital to wait upon the governor, they are usually headed by Mrs. Chancellor. She steers committees, makes speeches, draws up petitions and is in general a *force majeure* on the side of the angels.

Cynthia, however, has two small children—so the only thing likely to be requested of her in the way of civic up lift would be the making of posters. And that Mrs. Chancellor could have asked for over the phone.

"Maybe she wants you to run for office," I said.

Cynthia shrugged.

"I don't know. She sounded busy and purposeful, but then, she always does."

Although Mrs. Chancellor's field of operations includes most of the county, she actually lives in the neighboring town of Thrumborough. She is, in fact, president of the Women's Liberal Club of Thrumborough, although the distinction bears about the same relation to the rest of her agenda as Warden of the Cinque Ports did to Winston Churchill's.

The sociologists (and I wonder if their vogue will hold out for another ten years) generally seem to write about Suburbia as if it were all of a piece. Actually, the metropolis has its suburbs, and then the suburbs in turn have *their* suburbs—and Thrumborough is a suburb of ours. Until fairly recently (from the historic point of view), we were a sleepy little upcounty city with a small woodworking plant and a shaded main street where General Grant granite alternated with little frame houses that had had store fronts built on to them. A few miles away from this giddy Rialto was a range of low, wooded hills with clefts and ravines. Here the wealthy of F. Scott Fitzgerald's day constructed Norman keeps and half-timbered residences that are known in Harry's office as "Center-hall Baronial."

Our main street is wide and treeless now, and lined with six-, seven- and eight-story office buildings whose modern façades make the idle stroller (if any such there be) feel rather as if he had gotten lost in a box of Saltines. Thrumborough, however, has suffered only the minimal invasion. Some of the estates have been divided up, and where once they stretched unbroken are now enormous ranch houses that no amount of curtaining can keep from looking like sixteen-car garages. The old grammar school has become a junior high, and the new grammar school cost three million dollars—and one wit is said to have remarked that people come and look at it by moonlight, as if it were the Taj Mahal.

Thrumborough, however, still has—as it has always had —only one little cloistered square devoted to commerce.

In this chaste rectangle, the druggist has a bow window and is called a chemist. The tailor, too, is in mellow red brick, and you go in under a snowy-white, classical pediment as you take the pater's Brooks Brothers vest to be beaten clean by the maidens of Nausicaä.

But a Women's Liberal Club?

"Que font-elles dans cette galère?"

In its own way, money, like war, is the great leveler. Writers write books that sell to Hollywood. Television producers are treated a little better than Bob Cratchit. Designers work for oil companies and even anthropologists beat tom-toms for the large foundations. Some of these gentlemen may have worn their Stevenson buttons on the under side of the lapel, like an F.B.I. badge, but everyone knows that no good American gives orders to the little woman.

One may laugh at Thrumborough. In fact, everybody does. But as Cynthia's doorbell rang and the expected visitor came in with a swirl of perfume, veil and furs that drooped from a rather bony shoulder, I reflected that both Cynthia and I had for Mrs. Brock Chancellor the respect that homebodies feel for the movers and shakers. In addition, I felt—and I believed I could sense that Cynthia felt—a basic sympathy with the caller. Her son and daughter are almost grown up; she is too well off to make her own soap in a cauldron as the rest of us have to do; and her husband, despite the Byronic name, is gentle and drippy, like a February thaw. Why should she not be a dynamo? The work needs to be done; and one doubts that she is ever sufficiently thanked for it.

Cynthia had the tea all ready, so we plunged immediately into the amenities of sandwich-passing. This was the first time I had seen Mrs. Chancellor up close, and I examined her with interest. Her useful life has not given her the appearance of St. Cecilia at the organ. While she has flashing white teeth, good skin and eyes as blue as Young Cat's, her jaw is long, narrow and pugnacious and her manner calculated to disabuse instantly anyone who might think a mink-clad lady from Thrumborough cannot handle a surly attendant at the county almshouse.

Mrs. Chancellor soon came to the point. She had seen the piece about Great-aunt Persis in *Time* and the note in the local paper saying that Cynthia and Russ would be entertaining Cynthia's great-aunt for two weeks in the fall. Mrs. Chancellor wanted Great-aunt Persis to speak at a fund-raising luncheon of the Women's Liberal Club of Thrumborough.

"Of course," she said, "we wouldn't be able to pay her anything . . ." and she enveloped both Cynthia and me in an azure glance that was a little like shock treatment.

"I'm so sorry."

Cynthia's voice conveyed genuine regret.

"The paper was wrong. The plans have been changed. My aunt is only coming here to dinner and to stay over one night."

Mrs. Chancellor was not even momentarily daunted.

"Perhaps she could come early that day and speak at lunch. Or stay over till past lunchtime the next day. We could fetch her from anywhere and drive her any place she wants to go. And we could make it any day she wants."

Cynthia frowned and rubbed her forehead in perplexity.

"My aunt is seventy years old," she said. "And I know she already has a lot to do on this trip."

Mrs. Chancellor flashed a brilliant smile.

"My dear," she said, "you're thinking that I'm a reptile,

and I am. I admit it freely. I'm invading the privacy of your visit with your aunt. I'm exploiting an old lady . . ."

Her fingers played vigorously with the crystal beads around her neck.

"Although," she continued, "I simply cannot think of her as more than fifty."

Cynthia smiled with affection and pride.

"Neither can I," she said. "When you think of the cult of youth in this country . . ."

For a split second Mrs. Chancellor's face seemed to indicate that she had not thought of it, and I wondered if all that accomplishment was mindless and compulsive, but she went on persuasively.

"I wouldn't do it if there weren't a great need. You simply have no idea what your aunt can do for us in terms of morale building."

One does not automatically associate Thrumborough with the idea of shattered morale, so I guess both Cynthia and I looked a query.

"At first, the club wasn't even allowed a place to meet," Mrs. Chancellor continued.

"What?" I said.

"We wanted to rent a vacant store, or maybe a part of that old carriage house back of the golf club, and nobody would rent space for us to meet in. And you know you really can't have headquarters in somebody's house."

"Gosh!"

Cynthia's voice was awed.

"Finally, the Presbyterians let us have a bit of their old Parish Hall when they moved into the new one."

Mrs. Chancellor saw that she was making an impression on Cynthia and pressed her advantage.

"We could make such a big thing of it," she urged.

"We'd have the *Time* thing reprinted. People would come from all over the county. And," she added, rapidly turning an unlit cigarette end over end, "it would really make us felt."

"What would you want my aunt to talk on?" Cynthia asked.

"Anything. Reading-for-India. Nehru. Madame Chiang and Madame Sun Yat-sen. Foreign policy. Anything she wants."

"I suppose," Cynthia began, "you'd like me to write and ask her—"

She broke off.

"Oh, no, I couldn't!" she exclaimed. "It's too much. She'll only be here such a short time."

Mrs. Chancellor was shrewd enough not to say anything. She merely turned on her young hostess a blue, expectant gaze.

"Of course," Cynthia continued reflectively, "Aunt Persis is used to giving speeches. She'd take it in stride."

The idea of succoring the beleaguered liberals of Solvency Township clearly appealed to Cynthia. On the other hand, it was, of course, Great-aunt Persis who would be doing the succoring.

"I know what you're thinking," Mrs. Chancellor said. "How can we ask the head of Reading-for-India to be bothered about a few female do-gooders in Thrumborough, of all places?"

Cynthia shook her head.

"It isn't that. She always thinks—"

Cynthia laced her long and slightly paint-stained fingers together.

"—in the immediate human terms."

She sighed.

"The thing is," she went on, "that I'm pretty sure she'd do it, if I asked her."

"Not necessarily," I interjected. "One has the feeling that Great-aunt Persis has a mind of her own. If she really feels unable or unwilling to do it, she probably will not palter with the truth."

Cynthia gave me a relieved look.

"Well . . ." she said.

Mrs. Chancellor saw that she had won her point, and her smile made the normal headlight look like a miner's candle.

"Then you'll write and ask?" she said.

"I'm still reluctant," Cynthia answered, "but I will."

The visitor rose.

"Shall I write, too? Or wait till later?"

"Wait till later," Cynthia said.

"If she says she'll do it," Mrs. Chancellor remarked, gathering up bag and gloves, "we'll make a terrific thing of it."

She gave us one last blue glance, shouldered her way into a congeries of silken pelts that looked like the answer to a trapper's prayer, and was gone.

Later, when Harry came home and we were having our glass of wine and some toothsome canapés I had made from water chestnuts and bacon, I told him about the afternoon.

Instead of smiling responsively, as I had expected, he looked glum.

"What's the matter?" I said—a little snappishly, because I was beginning to feel a qualm of doubt. "Do you think we shouldn't have given in to the pressure?"

77

"It's not that," he replied. "It's only that Mrs. Chancellor and Great-aunt Persis just don't dovetail in the mind."

But I was hungry and rather greedily preoccupied with thoughts of dinner, and I brushed the idea aside.

"Oh, be fair!" I said. "Maida Chancellor works hard. She's entitled to Great-aunt Persis. Besides, what could happen?"

April 25th ✕ This little study of Harry's is hot in summer and cold in winter, and is besides an architectural excrescence that spoils the exterior lines of the house. And yet I like it, although none of the many magazines devoted to home improvement would tolerate it for a minute. They would either get a loan from the bank and tear it down or, if they were in a pennypinching mood, they would turn it into a very special alcove, with museum lighting, for the Marster's collection of beer steins.

But I like to speculate on what the original builder had in mind, thirty years ago, when he constructed this area which is too large for a closet and too small for a second chair. And sometimes I like to think that he had a burst of prescience and built this little room for just exactly what it is being used for now—a place where a fugitive from the good life, the children being at school and the men away at business, could sit down quietly and bite the many hands that feed her.

April 26th ✕ One of the things upon which I brooded lightly—as I did the ellipse this morning of fish store, drug store, tailor, hardware, shoe repair and Plethora, Incorporated—was the variety of attitudes displayed by policemen at school crossings. Some officers walk right across the street with the children, bending over to hear what they have to say and occasionally placing a hand lightly on a sweater-clad shoulder. Others, however, are lofty and impatient. These latter stand in the middle of the intersection, gesturing with hauteur and scowling at dawdlers, foot-draggers and inspectors of bugs and pebbles.

The most interesting class, however, is the class which is not involved enough even to be impatient. These burly protectors are totally withdrawn. They teeter on the edge of the curb, and convey by an utter impassivity of mien that they are only there to pick up the arms and legs after the motorists have driven up on the sidewalk and mowed the scholars down.

April 29th ❧ There is a house a little farther down the hill which Harry and I in our walks have often remarked upon as being comfortable and attractive-looking. It has a "For Sale" sign on it now, which evokes the frightening reflection that although the initials most frequently associated with the suburbs are P.T.A., the initials that really haunt the suburbs are P.T.U., standing for Permanent Talented Unemployed.

What we know around here but seldom discuss in detail is that once a man over thirty-five slips through one of the holes in The Affluent Society, it is almost impossible for him to get back in at the same level. The man who owns the house which has just come on the market is reputed to speak six languages—he was in the export business—but he has been out of work for what seems like nearly a year now. On the commuter trains, the dirty word is not anything that people write on the cement walls of underpasses. It is "résumé."

May 1st ✎ Cynthia has heard from Great-aunt Persis, who cheerfully expresses herself as willing to address our friend's liberal synod. It will require some rearrangements, for Aunt Persis's schedule is so intricate that it cannot be lightly tampered with, but Cynthia is going to take care of things.

May 4th ✎ Our whole neighborhood and even the development is a pageant of apple blossom, mountain pink, basket-of-gold, bleeding-heart, tulip, forget-me-not and the fallen stars of dogwood. A sobering circumstance, however, keeps me from getting too much intoxicated with petal and zephyr.

The circumstance is Mr. and Mrs. Sine Qua.

Mr. and Mrs. Sine Qua live next door to us, and are so named because a sine qua is the opposite of a sine qua non—a without-which one would be happy. In the winter, we are almost unaware of Mr. and Mrs. Sine Qua, for they seem never to come out, but in the summer they pass to and fro a bit and favor us with baleful stares—the serpents in our Eden.

It may be said of the Sine Quas that they were boobytrapped, for in the beginning they seemed innocent enough. They are a tall couple of nebulous age; they both wear mildew-colored clothes which are superlatively neat; and Mrs. Sine Qua, though not fat, is so tightly girdled that, seen from the rear, she looks like a tongue depressor. The Sine Quas have no childen and no pets and appear to live like recluses. No matter how hot the weather, they are never seen relaxed in deck chairs on the grass, and they appear on their porch only long enough to sweep it. A gardener comes once a week to take care of their lawn and shrubbery, so no one has any leaning-on-the-rake conversations with them.

By popular report, Mr. and Mrs. Sine Qua are pathologically shy and their life is centered on taking care of their possessions. I can vouch in part for the shyness, for once when Mrs. S. was in the hospital with appendicitis, I took some cookies over to her husband, and accepting his acknowledgments was like watching an oyster struggle to say thank you. Mrs. Sine Qua is the kind of housekeeper who washes the mailbox and scrubs the outside of the front door—a refinement which is, to say the least of it, not usual on our street. However, Harry and I always said hello when we saw them, and beyond that, season in and season out, we never gave the Sine Quas another thought.

Then one Saturday noon about two years ago, we came home from doing errands and while I was in the kitchen decanting groceries I heard Harry say, "Helen!" in a strangled voice. Thinking of heart attacks, I raced to his side, but he was looking out the window. I looked, too—and recoiled in utter disbelief. Mr. and Mrs. Sine Qua, neat as ever, were just completing the erection of a fence between their property and ours, and the fence was not neat.

We goggled at it.

It was not the romantic picket. It was not the nobly simple rail. It was not the privacy-securing split sapling. It was a sort of embroidered chicken wire, leaning a bit here and there, where they had not been able to get the posts quite upright, and clumsily pieced at one end. Slashing across the granite outcroppings of our two little hilltop lots, the effect was as if someone had tacked a sleazy pink ruffle on one of those Cézanne paintings of rock and pine.

And one thing I realized instantly: we were not going to be able to efface this monstrosity with Mantegna swags of fruit and flowers, because under our trees, nothing will grow any higher than a violet.

"But why didn't they *say* something?" I cried.

Mr. and Mrs. Sine Qua stood back and appeared to be admiring their handiwork. Then they began picking up tools.

"My eyes stumble on it," I said.

Slowly withdrawing, the Sine Quas went indoors.

"Is it the affront direct?" Harry said. "Or what?"

I felt the sting of tears.

"It's Tobacco Road," I said. "They've made us into a rural slum."

"But why?" Harry said.

The more we looked, the more confused and emotional we felt.

"If it's sagging now," I said, "what will it be at the end of a long winter?"

"Do you want to move back to the city?" Harry asked with rueful humor.

"I don't understand it," I said.

Harry looked at me and snapped his fingers. Then, with-

out a word, he walked determinedly out of the house and
—I saw through the window—up the Sine Qua walk.
Their screen door swung open for him before he rang
the bell, as if he had been expected. I went back to the
kitchen and started putting away groceries, moving in a
state of suspended feeling.

I had expected Harry to be gone at least half an hour,
but he was back in a very few minutes, looking daunted.

"What?" I asked, all eagerness.

He tapped his forehead significantly, and I frowned in
bewilderment. What he seemed to be conveying did not
jibe with the demure, obscure, almost invisible Sine Quas.

"She," Harry said elliptically.

"Say what you mean," I pleaded.

Harry gave a minute shiver.

"I went in very cheerfully," he said, "and made a little
joke about good fences making good neighbors."

"What's it like inside?"

He shrugged. "Who knows?"

I was disappointed, considering this a notable failure
of reconnaissance, but I said nothing.

"The alleged man of the house," Harry elucidated,
"was nervous. He started right in talking about how much
money the fence had cost and how difficult it had been to
put up."

Harry paused.

"But *she*—" he said.

"What did she say?"

"Well," he continued, "I kept right on being the good
mixer and the hearty extrovert, and I said after all there
wasn't really any need for a fence there, because we don't
have a dog."

He rubbed his forehead.

"I was very appealing," he said. "I really was."

I waited in silence for what was to come next. Clearly, Harry had had a shock.

He moved his shoulders.

"She said, 'That fence will serve its purpose.' "

Our neighbor's utterance, as evoked by Harry, was prim to the point of prissiness, but it had a thin-lipped, sadistic relish about it that would have gotten a standing ovation at a school for gauleiters.

"So," Harry said, "I just looked at her, kind of stupidly, and she said, 'The leaves . . . from your trees . . . are blowing . . . onto my property.' "

It took Harry and me some days to live through our juicy fantasies of revenge and achieve a state of philosophical resignation about the Sine Qua fence. Our friends and acquaintances were sympathetic, particularly about the sneak-attack aspect of the event. However, compared to supporting the aged parents or getting along with a difficult boss, an unsightly fence is a very small Calvary indeed.

We struggled manfully for perspective.

We would not take it personally, we assured each other. Mrs. S. was clearly reacting, not to us, but to some domineering parent-figure in her past. Everybody has these troubles in the suburbs, we said.

Psychologically, we said, the fence was an attempt to attract attention; and as the Sine Quas are bounded on their other two sides by a towering forest of honeysuckle, ours was the only border where notice would be taken.

After a few days, we had lathered ourselves into a state of compassion and understanding that verged on the saintly. But then Harry, who was just not born to be a victim, brought us back to earth.

The following Saturday morning was a beautiful day. I was standing in the front doorway, feeling glad to be alive. Harry was down by the retaining wall next to the sidewalk, hefting a spading fork and pondering on whether to court a hernia by spading over our root-filled soil. Suddenly the Sine Qua door opened and Mrs. Sine Qua made one of her rare appearances.

Shimmering with spite and glittering with triumphant malice, she progressed down her walk and turned in our direction. Harry and I stood in uncertain silence, and then as the lady swept past us and the boardlike rear elevation came into view, Harry spoke.

"You can win, Winsocki," he said to the stiffly retreating figure. "You're certainly buckled down."

May 8th 〜 Last night was the occasion of the Brownie and Girl Scout father-daughter dinner, a discreet Saturnalia which afflicts many fathers with dat ole debbil, "mingled emotions," but which has a singular purity of meaning for the little girls. The eyes of Manhood are upon them, and they show off.

There was much that Harry did not need to describe when he came home, for the affair was held in the basement of the Samuel T. Atkinson Grade School. That stately pleasure dome I know well. The Samuel T. Atkinson basement has a low ceiling and a great many pillars, which give it a strong resemblance to a crypt. However, the walls and ceiling are painted yellow, with a dado of defiant maroon, so it seems like a crypt for the bones of people who were not very much mourned—hanging judges, perhaps, or publicity seekers, or faceless accusers in "loyalty" trials.

Harry waved a happy and buoyantly treading Cora upstairs—she looked very elfin in her Brownie uniform—and sat down.

"The *noise!*" he said.

"I know," I replied.

And indeed, I do. I have been to Children's Crusades in that basement, and that particular kind of incessant and echoing uproar makes me feel like a pencil being sharpened. I keep thinking that the clamor will suddenly stop, and there I will be with the top of my head honed to a fine, needlelike point.

The fathers, according to Harry, stood about between the long tables and benches looking tentative. The usual twilight restoratives—the drink, the shirt-sleeved ease, the hot dinner—were not available or immediately in prospect; and it is hard, in a boiler factory, to introduce yourself to strangers and start up a conversation.

However, at Harry's and Cora's table, one little Brownie broke the social ice—although not intentionally. Just as the sandwiches brought from home were being opened and the school-basement coffee was being handed around, a man slid into the end seat. He was rapturously welcomed by the girl-child next to him. The newcomer had been seated less than a minute, however, when his face altered. Rolling over on the beam-end, like a freighter in a heavy sea, he put an exploratory hand on the bench.

"Chewing gum!" he exploded. "And I flew all the way in from Ohio!"

One glance was enough to tell who had put the chewing gum there, but before Poppa could proceed with the traumatizing comment he obviously had in mind, a man sitting two or three places down said, "Hold hard, mate! I've got some Carbona in the car."

Brownies were sent for the Carbona, the chewing gum was removed, two Lily cups full of milk were knocked over in the excitement . . . "and we ended up," Harry said, "as cozy as a complement of steerage passengers."

The slight meal disposed of, two Girl Scout apparatchiks—by which seditious name Harry refers to Neighborhood Chairwomen—made speeches of welcome. Then the Girl Scouts entertained.

The first offering was an ill-rehearsed and hastily costumed dramatization of *The Sleeping Beauty*. Giggles, stumbles and the necessity for virtually uninterrupted prompting made it seem, Harry said, interminable. But the second skit, by another troop, had bite. A Scout gotten up with eyeglasses and charcoal mustache to approximate the usual television scientist came out and said, "I represent the new detergent, Liquid Dirt. Liquid Dirt is something new! It contains no secret ingredients. It contains no well-known ingredients. Liquid Dirt contains *absolutely no ingredients*."

The point of the sketch was that a housewife, who was supposed to determine which pillow case was washed in Liquid Dirt and which in Brand X, made the wrong choice, and the scientist shot her. By Harry's account, the little vignette had been carefully prepared and was executed with a certain amount of style, but that was perhaps not the only reason why the fathers applauded to the echo.

May 9th ~~ At the end of a rainy day in May, the trees and grass are such a vivid, emerald green that they seem in sheer brilliance to be fighting off the dusk. And almost winning.

May 10th 〜 I went to the dentist last week, responding rather more promptly than usual to his printed invitation because I had been having shooting pains in one of the lower incisors.

I did not, however, tell the Bad Samaritan about these pains, figuring that with his X-rays and poking and probing he would be sure to uncover the difficulty and say—with the morbid satisfaction of his kind—"Ummm, this has been giving you trouble."

After that, I looked forward to one of those sequences over which, as nineteenth-century authors used to remark, it would be kinder to draw the curtain; for the pain was in a tooth that had proved resistant to Novocaine.

But the dentist did not find anything.

Not that he did not try. He all but took my teeth out and let them drip through his fingers, but he could locate only one small cavity way in the back. After he had filled this and cleaned them, he asked in routine and unexpectant fashion, "Anything been giving you trouble?"

And I looked him right in the eye and said, "No."

One hears people speak of an actor's actor or a writer's writer. Is there such a thing as a craven's craven?

The unnerving part of the whole business—to one brought up in a Puritan frame of reference about reward and punishment—is that ever since I told this whopper, the tooth has not hurt.

May 14th ❧ We cleaned off the porch yesterday, bought some pots of ivy for the wall brackets, and moved the porch furniture out. It is still too cool to eat there, but we all move on a slightly springier metatarsal because our leaf-embowered summer life is about to begin.

May 15th ❧ I went into a downtown department store today in search of sheets for Saber-foot Cora, who does not like to cut her toenails and whose bed linen is usually all streamers, like a Maypole. Three aisles over, Mrs. Brock Chancellor was being shown bedspreads. It is an odd thing, but I could swear she saw me and pretended not to. She suddenly seemed to get elaborately and self-consciously absorbed.

I must be imagining things.

May 18th ❧ "Bad pussy!" I said. "Bad! *Bad!*"

"What did they do?" said Cora as I came into the dining room.

"The Senior shoved the Junior away and took his supper."

Cora looked at Harry.

"That's our Mommy," she said. "Always for the under-cat."

I do not, I realize, have to worry unduly about Cora's growing up too soon and being lost to us too immediately. Finding, to her surprise and delight, that the grownups considered this a bon mot, she repeated it four times within the next half hour.

At what age, I wonder, does one learn that a joke is good for only one go-round with any given audience? I can remember *not* knowing it. I can remember being a child, and being shocked at the grownups because—profligates that they were—they let funny lines go down into oblivion all sloshing and drippy with unmilked laughs. Harry got impatient with Cora for spoiling the artistic purity of her original effect, but I knew how she felt. Grownups know where jokes come from, and can afford to wait in confidence and relaxation for the next one, but to a child, there may never *be* another.

May 20th ❧ Cora has been passing her arithmetic tests by a comfortable margin for ten days now, and Mrs. Elliott sent word today that we might stop the drill. Cora herself had a glint of pride and self-esteem in her blue-grey eye as she delivered this welcome communication. As for Harry and me, we joined hands and danced around the coffee table.

Cora's arithmetic drill started out well enough, with all concerned thinking highly of one another; but owing to the fact that our daughter did not seem to learn very fast, the drill degenerated into something that must have had Madame Montessori and Kittredge of Harvard turning in their graves.

Parent #1, saturated in advance with tedium and ennui, would seat itself and begin the liturgy.

"Four plus two? Eight plus five? Six take-away three?"

(We had to learn to say "take-away" instead of "minus.")

Three or four minutes were usually required to reach

the point where Cora—confronted with, say, six plus three—faltered.

Parent #1, though thinking wistfully of the intoxicating life and Mardi Gras excitements of prisoners picking oakum, was still doggedly simulating encouragement and cheer.

"Come now! Six plus three. You know it, darling."

This, of course, is a flat lie. Darling did not know it yesterday, and there is no reason to suppose that the vacant attic underneath that golden-brown thatch has suddenly filled up overnight with intellectual treasure.

"Eight?" says the Madame Curie of the Samuel T. Atkinson Grade School.

By this time, Parent #1 is having to keep a very tight rein on sensations of impatience and disgust. But shored up by the tradition of noblesse oblige, he or she says, "Let's skip that one for a while and do the others."

The situation, however, has already degenerated into an educational Passchendaele. Children are totally unappreciative of the gallantry involved in faking interest about a grinding monotony. They do not want you to succeed in concealing impatience. They want you not to *be* impatient.

Cora answers a few more questions correctly, but only after long hesitations, and suddenly, with the irrationality of childhood, her eyes begin to fill with tears. Irritated by the brimming orbs, Parent #1 says abruptly, "Six plus three?"

"I dough know anything when you ack that way!"

Cora's face is wet and threatening, like the reef of Norman's Woe.

Parent #1 clenches fists in helpless fury because the sacrificial gesture is so clearly going to waste.

"Well, for heaven's sake!" he or she says angrily. "You'll get left back if you don't learn it. Six plus three, count it on your fingers if you have to, but get an answer!"

At the mention of being left back, Cora starts to cry in real earnest and Parent #1 stalks out onto the porch or into the kitchen and stands there breathing hard.

"Don't tell me," says Parent #1 grimly, "that Socrates corrupted the youth of Athens. It was the other way round."

At this point, Parent #2 takes over. (These roles are interchangeable, and, as a matter of fact, anybody can get into this club.)

Armed with Kleenex, a benevolent smile and the serene conviction that he or she is about to make Mr. Chips look like King Herod, Parent #2 sits down next to the tear-sodden child.

It takes about five minutes for Parent #2's hubris to encounter the classic and customary fate. Parent #2 has overlooked the fact that he or she has also had a nerve-shattering surfeit of addition and subtraction. By extremely perceptible gradations, the kindly guidance, the firm but gentle tuition, is metamorphosed into reckless, old-fashioned child-berating. (The kind of wounding and abrasive taunts, in fact, that produced Winston Churchill, Mark Twain, George Orwell and other family disgraces.)

In no time at all, Parent #2 also strides out onto the porch or into the kitchen and stands there breathing hard. Cora, having exhausted the available supply of Oxford dons, lies on the couch sobbing. But within the minute, there is a sound from inside as of Ben-Hur urging the chariot horses into the place by the rail. It is a television commercial, the young arithmetician having defiantly turned on the twenty-one-inch tranquilizer, although this is not one of the permitted hours.

But Parent #2 does not even notice.

"She doesn't try!" says Parent #2. "She doesn't try!"

However, though stormed at by shot and shell, Cora has somehow managed to master fourth-grade arithmetic.

"She did it!" Harry exclaimed triumphantly, scooping his daughter into an embrace and kissing the top of her head.

"Yes," I replied. "Magna cum louder."

May 25th ❧ The bathroom curtains having been laundered to the point of dissolution, I went to a dry-goods store this morning to get dotted Swiss for new ones. To my sorrow, I was informed that dotted Swiss has become so out of date that only with determination—and possibly a little help from the Swiss consulate—can it be tracked down in stores that make a special point of carrying "old-fashioned cottons."

With the usual contemporary irony, the dry-goods store —while not having the simple thing I *did* want—was oppressively overstocked with a great deal I wanted no part of. Foreign observers have not yet been rude enough to point it out, but it is certain that many of them have had the idea: American stores are reminiscent of overloaded stomachs and, far from suggesting civilization, convey to the detached mind a hint of imminent social disaster.

The Rising Gorge Dry-goods Shop, where I was this morning, had shelves crammed and tables heaped with adjectival fabrics—"polished" broadcloth . . . "crease-re-

sistant" linen . . . "bouclé" this . . . "vat-dyed" that
. . . "fiber-glass" the other. Near the door on one side, a
large bin contained foam-rubber pillows in triangles and
circles. Farther back was a sort of museum exhibit of de-
vices and gadgets for making pinch pleats (omitting, of
course, the human thumb and forefinger). Beyond the
pleats, a big board displayed assorted rods for draw curtains.

Along the back wall was an array, tiered like a Ganges
bathing ghat, of thread, zippers, tapes and ribbons. It ad-
joined an offering of scissors over which Delilah could
have been imagined licking her lips. On the other side
wall, models of valances alternated with small-scale samples of curtain styles. Across from the cushion bin, and
taking up a good deal of space, was a kind of seamstress's
Library of Congress of trimming and ornament—ruffles,
edgings, laces, upholstery bindings, insertions, weltings,
beadings and an infinite variety of fringe and tassel.

Compelled, in the midst of this equatorial luxuriance, to
settle for organdy ("permanent-finish") instead of dotted
Swiss, I instinctively thought of my recurrent fantasy of
the F.O.O.P.

(I pronounce the initials and call it Foop.)

This fantasy first came to mind when we had just
moved to the suburbs and I took my sewing machine to
the sales-and-service place to be cleaned. The machine
was at that time nearly twenty years old, and I felt about it
as one ought to feel about machinery. It had worn well;
we had fought many a zipper together; I admired it and
had come to regard it as semi-human. But the salesman at
the sewing-machine store took my old friend out of its battered case, looked at it with curling lip, and shot me a
lightning glance. The glance palpably expected to encounter Silas Marner or some other celebrated skinflint.

"Bud!" said the salesman curtly over his shoulder.

A young man in work clothes emerged from the back room, looking very much out of place in the mirrored and carpeted sales salon.

"C'we clean this?" asked the salesman.

Bud surveyed the machine and then also gave me the "she-has-negotiable-securities-sewed-into-her-dirty-under-wear" look.

Returning his small but piercing eye to the sewing machine, Bud contemplated it woodenly, and then turned down the corners of his mouth and hunched his shoulders almost up to his ears.

"We can, if we *have* to," the gesture said, and with no spoken utterance, the gesturer returned to whatever Temple of Progress he inhabited in the rear.

The salesman wrote out a slip and I departed, having studiously pretended to be unaware of this byplay. But it was then that I first began to have the persistent daydream about the F.O.O.P.

In this fantasy, a day comes when the inhabitants of the United States begin to find little bits of torn paper everywhere, each with a message on it. These small communications materialize in every conceivable place. They seem to drift from nowhere onto the seats of buses. They drop out of the pages of library books, and turn up in parked cars. They are tucked into the blotter on office desks, secreted upon the shelves of supermarkets and folded into the tissue paper of boxes that come from department stores. Each bit of paper contains the same message, and the message is always typed or handwritten, never commercially printed.

The message is "Watch for the F.O.O.P.!"

When it becomes apparent that this phenomenon is

pandemic, so to speak, there is a sweet disorder in the press. Some papers ascribe the mysterious communications to juvenile delinquents. Others talk of space men—of the Russians—of the beat generation—of the White Citizens' Councils—of the Mafia—of Walter Reuther—of a clever publicity stunt. But no further light is shed; and as no mystery can be discussed indefinitely without a resolution, the newspapers eventually prepare to bury the F.O.O.P., along with Judge Crater and the Marie Celeste.

Then a new development occurs.

A day dawns when the lady shoppers stay at home. The female consumers do not consume. The department stores are empty. The supermarkets echo. The discount houses are "bare ruined choirs."

The newspaper advertisements go unread. The television commercials are not turned on. The door-to-door vacuum-cleaner salesmen seem to be talking to primitives who live on earth floors. In the mailboxes, fistfuls of promotion material sit unattended in the dark. The free sample of Mr. Stiff, the Magic Embalming Fluid ("Praised Alike by the Kwik and the Ded") is kicked off the doorstep and into the bushes.

Something very like quiet falls over the noisy land, and in the lull can be heard a sound of jingling as the Colonel's lady and Judy O'Grady take baskets of nickels, dimes and quarters into the garden and bury them under the laburnums.

By nightfall, the United States is a changed country. Lysistrata rides again, and the hand that rocks the cradle, rocks the cradle.

By nightfall, nobody is in business in the U.S.A. except a couple of Thrift Shops, some church rummage sales and that corps of the Salvation Army that sells used furniture and old clothes.

The evening papers have but one headline.

They set it in the type they last dug out for the *Lusitania*.

"F. O. O. P.!"   [it says]

"THE FORCES OF ORGANIZED

PENURY"

Ho, hum! It is one of the functions of dreams, the psychologists say, to relieve tension; and this one certainly relieves mine.

May 28th One of the reasons for moving out of the city is fresh air, and that part of the Suburbia deal really comes off—although it is seldom mentioned in the discussions of dormitory towns. After dinner this evening, I stood in our front yard in the spring twilight, and all down the hill people were out of doors, watering lawns, edging turf and setting out plants. On the slanting sidewalk, Cora and her friends played hopscotch and some younger children toiled up the slope with their small-size bicycles like a collection of diminutive Sisyphuses. Next door (the other side from the Sine Quas) a catbird in a birdbath scattered crystal into the dusk.

In the late spring, just before the first firefly is seen and the first cricket heard, darkness at the end of day has a particularly delicate way of arriving. It does not, as in the maturer season, plump down with a voluptuous smack and make the house lights seem like jewelry set off by black velvet. Rather, spring darkness comes with an exquisite diffidence—stealing out in diaphanous filaments from under the bushes and settling like a breath or a sigh between the houses and around the plants. The dark seems to mingle with the light streaming from the windows, so that the house lights as seen from the garden are dilute and lemony instead of blazing, while the blackness itself is suffused with luminosity.

As a lover of Verdi opera and a devotee of the withered-marble smell of museums, I am not one to sell the great city short; but the coming of a spring night to the suburbs is not wholly banal and commonplace, and let the arbiters of taste and the Great Social Thinkers not forget it.

June 2nd ⮞ Yesterday afternoon.

I was cleaning the seats of the dining-room chairs—breathing a little shallowly because of all the stories about people who have died from the fumes of carbon tetrachloride—when the doorbell gave a brief tinkle and Cynthia walked in. She looked ghastly. Her head with the golden hair drooped like a columbine and the skin under her eyes was blue.

"Gosh!" I said, going toward her.

She had on her good linen dress, I noticed. Suddenly, as she dropped into a chair in the living room, I had a horrible thought.

"Cynthia! Where are the boys?"

"Oh, they're all right. It isn't that. I left them up the street."

I relaxed and waited.

"It's Mrs. Chancellor. She asked if she could come over to discuss something private and very important."

I remembered that not-meeting-of-the-eyes in the department store and Harry's glum premonition about not dovetailing, but even at that, I was not prepared.

"It seems the invitation to Aunt Persis has been withdrawn."

For the first split second, it was quite meaningless.

"What?" I said.

Then the sounds began to come into focus.

"No!"

I began stammering.

"But . . . You don't . . . They can't . . ."

Cynthia had been regarding the hands in her lap, but now she raised her head and looked directly at me.

"It's the American Legion," she said. "They object."

Outside the window, the nubile sunlight of early summer shone on stainless grass and trees, and across the street a crimson rambler, urgent as the trumpets at a coronation, foamed on a white trellis.

"The Women's Liberal Club of Thrumborough hopes I will understand. Naturally, they are terribly embarrassed."

I stared at her.

"But that's *obscene!*" I said.

Cynthia gave me a shaky smile.

"I'm glad you feel the same way. I thought maybe I was overreacting because she's my aunt."

"But she changed her whole schedule to fit them in!"

Cynthia's mouth tightened.

"The sheer, plowboy boorishness!" I said hotly.

I got up from my chair and started to walk around.

"I can't believe it."

The girl remained silent.

"And from Thrumborough, the home of the aristocrats!" I said.

In her pale face, Cynthia's nostrils flared with contempt.

"What is . . . ?" I began.

I loathed putting the question. Merely to ask it seemed a defilement in itself.

"What is the Legion's objection?"

Cynthia took a breath.

"That Aunt Persis is a longtime associate of Chinese Communists."

"And of Chinese Nationalists, too!" I burst out. "For heaven's sake! She was raised in China. She was married to a missionary bishop. She's a missionary herself, in a way."

"My aunt," Cynthia said wryly, "has spoken to too many groups. So they've got her on a list."

Cynthia's eyes suddenly filled with tears, and she angrily shook them away. I knew by instinct what she was feeling. We had been so determined not to see in Mrs. Brock Chancellor the standard caricature of the American clubwoman. We had been so eager to believe that what she did was based on principle and conviction and not on the compulsive display of vitality. And the result of this infatuation—this besotted and benighted Christian charity—was to let Great-aunt Persis in for a choice bit of moral squalor.

To break this line of thought, I asked Cynthia what the Legion was proposing to do.

"Write letters to the paper," she said.

We looked at each other. We did not have to say anything. The local paper had had feelings akin to a schoolgirl crush about Senator McCarthy.

"We'd better have some coffee," I said. "I'll put water on."

When I came back, Cynthia said, "She was really upset. You could see that."

"Hah!"

"But at the same time, she secretly thought she was handling it pretty well. You could see that, too."

I kneaded the back of my neck, where the muscles felt as if I had just built two or three pyramids.

"Come in the kitchen," I said. "I can always think better in the kitchen."

We pulled chairs up to the kitchen table and I asked, "What's her excuse? What's her justification for—for this behavior?"

"The Women's Liberal Club is a small and struggling organization. They can't afford to get the Legion angry at them."

Outside the sun had begun to wester, and a little breeze stirred the window curtain with a faint adumbration of evening. In a nearby tree a robin burst out into his long, rocking-horse lilt, and when at length he stopped, I could hear a woodpecker drilling.

"She believes," Cynthia said, "that Aunt Persis, with all her experience, might be the first to understand. If the club had a big membership and a terrific morale, and had been organized a long time—"

"Don't tell me," I said. "They'd have fought the Legion to a standstill. And how her blue eyes sparkled as she said it!"

"If they go through with their plans about having Aunt Persis, Mrs. Chancellor is sure that pressure will be brought to have their meeting place taken away from them."

"And in all of Thrumborough," I asked, "they can't find one little Navajo hogan where the secretary could read the minutes?"

Cynthia smiled wanly.

"She and the Executive Committee thrashed it out and thrashed it out. They believe there's a real need for a liberal club in Thrumborough, and a real chance of building one up to be active and influential, but not if they let themselves get wiped out before they start."

"The poor sods!"

I poured coffee. I had given Cynthia the final little shove toward consenting to write to her great-aunt, and I felt just as responsible as she.

Cynthia looked down at the coffee and inattentively pushed it away.

"I don't know whether I'm being quite fair to her," she said. "She hasn't forgotten that she steam-rollered me into writing my aunt."

"Did she say so?"

"No. Not directly. But I could tell from her manner."

"Cynthia!" I exclaimed. "If the entire Western Hemisphere were against her, she ought to stand behind that invitation!"

Cynthia gave the sudden, convulsive yawn of tension.

"If they hold the meeting, the Legion will picket it." She spoke almost absent-mindedly.

"Let me get this straight," I said. "They actually aren't going to have this meeting?"

"No. They aren't."

"And who," I asked sardonically, "is supposed to tell Great-aunt Persis that she is now a drug on the market?"

Cynthia sat up straight.

"That wasn't decided."

"Cynthia!"

"She said maybe we could put our heads together and think up some excuse, and I said, 'What excuse!' "

Her eyes flashed like scimitars.

"So," she added scornfully, "it was left up in the air.

"As a matter of fact," she continued after a moment, "it was all very inconclusive. I just wouldn't agree with anything she said. We went around in circles."

A little beyond the kitchen window, the last few lilacs of the season were blooming. As the level sunlight picked out the tapering mounds of blossom and the heart-shaped silver-washed leaves, I thought of the Whitman poem and then of the crisis Harry had been through about testifying —and I had a split second to be glad that I came to the Chancellor problem with something of a baptism of fire.

The gladness, however, was fleeting. It seemed to me that Mrs. Chancellor and her Executive Committee, meek Valkyries though they might be, had us boxed. Either we had to swallow a gross discourtesy to a wonderful person, or we had to assume a suppliant posture and beg Mrs. Brock Chancellor to let a woman fifty times her superior speak for nothing at a fund-raising lunch.

Cynthia got up and moved toward the door.

"Can you and Harry come over tonight?"

"Nothing could keep us away."

She gave me a grateful look.

"Never fear," I continued reassuringly. "We'll think of something. We'll drum on her chest with our tiny fists."

But as I stood in the doorway and watched Cynthia cross diagonally over the street, I was not optimistic. The whole neighborhood was a glory of green and gold, with late-afternoon sunlight on leaves at the very apex of their vernal freshness. I thought, however, of the parched villages of India and the letter that would have to be written to Great-aunt Persis, and I was not exactly palpitant with pride of country.

When Harry came home from the office, I said, "Guess who has just dumped an armload of carrion into our laps."

"The possibilities," he said with a smile, "are infinite."

But when I told him, he stopped smiling.

"They can't do that!" he said angrily.

However, on learning that we were going to Russ and Cynthia's later, he said he did not want to spoil his dinner by hashing the situation over and we talked of other things. I would not have thought I could be distracted from the sense of shock and the bleakness of the side being let down, but I was, and I even laughed when Harry swallowed the last of his sherry and said, "Ah, the good old Legion! We've got the hatred, so let's go into the dining room and eat the stalled ox."

Russ and Cynthia live in a house that was called—circa 1910, when it was built—a "bungalow." It is stucco, with a red tile roof, and the upper halves of the windows are cross-hatched. Instead of a railing, the porch has a swollen and dropsical cement parapet, and the porch roof is supported by pillars of incredible stubbiness. Inside, Cynthia has done wonders with a great deal of white paint, strong and simple colors, and interestingly textured fabrics, but the outside still automatically suggests that the occupants are reading Gene Stratton Porter and Harold Bell Wright.

When we had settled among the cool blues and the paintings of Cynthia's living room, Harry stretched his legs and said, "When confronted by a moral crisis, I always ask myself what Dr. Aspirin would do."

Everybody laughed, and I said, "That's easy. He'd say Great-aunt Persis is such a big woman . . . she wouldn't take any notice of this little pinprick . . . and neither should we."

"And let them get away with it?" asked Cynthia angrily.

"Steady on, old girl."

It was Russell speaking. Russell is a pipe-smoking Englishman whose transatlantic speech pattern always falls on my ear with a pleasant crispness—the verbal equivalent of celery crunching. He is almost as much older than Cynthia as I; he has a small, dark mustache; and although he is of the middle height, Cynthia is a little bit taller than he. The contracting parties to the marriage seem to regard this latter discrepancy as minor; but Cora, a ruthless and inflexible romantic, thinks it appalling and is always surprised to come home from school yet one more day and find Russell and Cynthia still united.

Harry spoke to Cynthia.

"It was implied," he asked, "that you and Mrs. Chancellor would have another meeting? That nothing had been really settled?"

Cynthia nodded.

"She understands that my family pride has been hurt. She's prepared to be infinitely patient."

Russell took his pipe from his mouth and cradled it in his hands.

"Actually," he said, "the person to discuss is not Aunt Persis, but Mrs. Chancellor."

"Ah," said Harry.

"She issued the invitation, and if her Executive Committee won't stand behind it, she ought to resign from the club."

Cynthia looked at her husband with admiration.

"I never thought of that," she said. "I was too much taken aback, I guess."

I felt a strong sensation of relief. Here at last would be a letter that could be written to Great-aunt Persis with some mitigation of the sense of shame. Or perhaps no letter would have to be written at all. Perhaps the ladies of the Executive Committee, faced with the loss of their president, would decide to endure the Legion's attentions to Great-aunt Persis.

My elation was only momentary, however. A dismaying consideration occurred to me.

"But wouldn't she have resigned already . . . if she were going to?"

Harry and Russ both spoke at once.

"Not necessarily," said Harry.

"It's amazing," said Russ, "how many people have to be nudged into what you'd expect them to do automatically."

"It's the times we live in," Harry said. "Resigning is a lost art. Look at old Sherman Adams. Had to be pulled up by the roots."

This new perspective on Mrs. Chancellor was bracing. Compared to the other things she did, being president of the Women's Liberal Club of Thrumborough was an insignificant office; and surely she would see right away that if we could write to Great-aunt Persis and say that the president of the organization had resigned in protest . . .

I felt much better.

There was something cheering in the idea that Cynthia need not meet Mrs. Chancellor on a purely complaining and negative basis. The ladies of Thrumborough might actually have a Liberal Club—bona fide and influential —if they could be got to endure the birth pains.

I stood up.

" 'Now sleeps the crimson petal, now the white,' " I said.

I gave Cynthia a quick pat on the cheek.

"And thank you very much, gentlemen," I added, "for the use of your little, flickering, fork-tongued minds."

June 6th 🙠 One difference between suburban life and city life is that in the suburbs, if you do not go away for your vacation, you disappoint people. Not that you are expected to take an expensive holiday. A cheap little jaunt like our forthcoming week on a dairy farm is quite acceptable. So is a fortnight with an embittered aunt who lives in a Charles Addams house and serves cheese parings and pemmican for dinner.

But merely to stay home for three weeks—going on picnics when it is clear and perhaps to a few museums or the theater—is to engender the suspicion that you are self-sufficient.

Harry and I, who hope by strenuous saving to get to Europe one of these years, have spent the past few holidays generating unease in the bosoms of the neighbors. This season, however, is different. There is not more rejoicing over slum children going to Fresh Air Camp than there is that the sealed-unit Fitzgibbonses have finally decided to leave home.

Consequently, when I announced up and down the road that we needed someone to take care of our cats, a pleasant young girl of high-school age was vouchsafed almost instantly—so happy were the local matrons to be spared one of the weeks of my husband lolling fecklessly in their midst. What song the Sirens sang has still to be divulged by Univac, but no one needs to wonder any more what name Achilles assumed when he hid himself among the women. It was "Harry Fitzgibbons."

June 8th ❧ The only provision store around here where men stand behind the counter, listen to your voice, and go fetch what you want is one that caters to the Thrumborough trade and charges ten and sometimes fifteen cents per item more than Plethora, Inc. (It is also rumored to practice fee-splitting with the conciergerie.) Nevertheless, there are times when I am strongly tempted to transfer my allegiance to this sedate clip joint. Plethora —with its Look-at-me! screams—wreaks havoc with the gentle sensuality of eating.

Plethora's Giant Canned Goods Sale, breaking upon a slumbrous world like Sarajevo, is succeeded by the Spring Frozen Food Sale; and then in rapid succession by the 1¢ Sale, the Manager's Sale and the Mix 'n Match Sale. The Mix 'n Match Sale proved to be beyond my intellectual capacity. I never succeeded in figuring out what was to be mix 'n matched. At the Manager's Sale, I did not buy so much as a single Tuffy Pot Scrubber, being unable to shake off a feeling that the whole thing was illicit and that the manager intended to scoop the receipts into a canvas sack and make off to South America.

A few weeks ago, Plethora's checkers were giving each departing customer a slip of paper marked with holes to be punched. This was part of a game you could play. The prizes (I believe) were fully articulated skeletons from the nearby medical school, which the winners could then have the fun and the challenge of fattening up on Plethora's weekly specials in milk, cheese and strictly fresh eggs.

Man does not live, however, by bread alone. This is a deplorable circumstance but not one calculated to defeat the promotion wallahs of a food chain. Plethora's clients are currently being introduced to twenty albums of the Great Classics in music—37¢ for the first album and $1.37 for each subsequent one (would be $3.98 if purchased in some Aeolian cave that does not stock paper towels and flank steak).

But the Great Classics of music I take in stride.

It was the encyclopedia that infuriated me.

Plethora is an organization where the language of Shakespeare is consistently debased into Veri-Thin, Parti-Snak, U-fill-it, Nu-Pak, Creami-Rich, Reddi-Wip, Sunkist, Jumbo-Rol and other combinations of vowel and consonant not recommended by the hard-working staff of the Samuel T. Atkinson Grade School. For the ruthless disseminators of these constructions to line themselves up even remotely with an encyclopedia was, to me, the greatest literary effrontery since the burning of the library at Alexandria.

"Why do you react so strongly?" Harry asked me once, speaking with the amused detachment of one who does not see Plethora, Inc. very often.

"It's the basic attitude," I replied. "They blind me with their eighteen-inch lettering. They deafen me with their yelling. And then they preen their feathers with their vicious black beak and pretend they are doing me a favor.

"And," I added scornfully, "they think I am so stupid that I won't see through it."

June 11th ❧ The movements of children up and down our street—the inexplicable clusterings and mysterious dispersals—remind me of the days when I was being educated and had to look at one-celled animals under a microscope.

You have your eye idly on somebody's driveway, baking and empty in the hot sun. Before you know it, big and little children have skimmed in from all directions, and are sitting, lying and standing—with their bicycles, express wagons, roller skates, plastic toys and baseball bats—all over the concrete and out into the macadam of the road. They settle down and seem to be at rest. Only an occasional outflung arm or the rolling over of a prostrate body, like the tentative vibration of the cilia, shows they are alive.

Then suddenly two of them dart off. In a minute, three more skate away in the opposite direction. A couple of toddlers start across the road, are yelled at, pause, and then continue on their way to extinction. Bicycles are pulled erect, leaned against and ultimately mounted. In six minutes only the detritus—a gimcrack pistol, an anomalous-looking stick and several good-sized stones—remains to show that anyone was there.

What brought them in the first place?

What caused them to depart?

Only a paramecium would know.

June 13th ❧ The Mrs. Chancellor affair.

No, not today. I am not, as the Jane Austen heroines say, in spirits for it.

The matter of Mrs. Chancellor has not, of course, the

same intensity as Harry's testifying for his friend. This time nobody's livelihood is threatened. But it is not cheering, definitely not cheering.

June 15th ❧ My duties as Sunday-school librarian are not onerous, but at the end of the school year, everybody ignores my tocsins about getting books back to the library and I have to hitch up old Dobbin and go after them. So I made my annual tour today, collecting *Heidi* and *Lad: A Dog* and handbooks on science and nature from homemakers who were profuse in their apologies. In the course of this circuit-riding, I noticed that three more churches are being built in the green stretches at the edge of town.

"On Sunday morning," I said to Harry, telling him about it, "prayer goes up from around here like smoke.

"It makes one think," I added, "of a kind of fall-out in reverse, with the Deity wondering nervously whether He has had more than the permissible amount of hypocrisy."

St. Euphoria, of course, is firmly anchored to the center of town by reason of the beauty and antiquity of its edifice. One of the first things Harry did when we joined the church was to suggest, with the authority of a regional planner, that St. E. acquire the adjoining property and make a parking lot of it—to be rented to sinners and publicans during the week and accommodate the parishioners on Sunday.

This idea stirred up the opposition usually evoked by a suggestion that is sensible but not currently fashionable. Dr. Aspirin, however, though a tepid shepherd in some ways, has at least the discernment to value the evocative symmetry of his building; and Harry was richly vindicated when St. Euphoria proved, on the trafficless Sabbath, rather quicker to get to than the little ranch church in the wildwood, the Corbusier temple in the dell.

I sometimes wonder whether this flight of the churches to the outskirts is unconsciously based on the principle: out of sight, out of mind. One of the things I like about St. Euphoria is that I see it almost every time I go downtown—either all of it, with its elm trees and graves counterbalancing the congested traffic and fretful streets, or at least a glimpse of its steeple soaring over the rather splintery buildings which surround it.

And apropos of churches moving into improved quarters, I still smile a little at Harry's remark about one of the new sanctuaries where the congregation, reacting against its former Victorian Gothic, put up an airy structure of Japanese arches and glass walls.

Harry shook his head and looked disapproving.

"It will never stand the gaff," he said, "when the Moslems stable their horses in it."

June 18th 〰 "Mommy, I'm *boiling!*" is the cry of Cora and her friends the instant they get home from school, and they forthwith peel off their crinolines and clothe themselves in postage-stamp shorts. I was watching a group of them this afternoon, clustered around somebody's new puppy. It was a veritable thicket of eight-, nine-, and ten-year-old legs, and looked, I thought, rather like a box of toothpicks come to Dunsinane.

June 20th ～ I saw a piece in the paper tonight in which a social scientist is reported as saying that the values of the American suburb—fun and comfort—have become the values the whole world seeks. I wish I could contribute to the fun and comfort by noting only that the fences in the development seem to groan under their burden of roses; that splendidly barbaric thunderstorms deploy overhead, between long, idyllic sequences of sunshine; and that the people across the street have such a splendid showing of delphinium and Madonna lily, I feel I ought to pay part of their taxes for the sheer ravishment of looking at it.

But Cynthia and I are finding our suburban fun and comfort diminished almost to the vanishing point by the Mrs. Chancellor situation.

The night after Mrs. C. dropped her bombshell, Harry's cousin Eugene stopped in. This is a fact I would probably not record—Eugene, though nice enough, having always seemed to Harry and me rather colorless—save that we got into an interesting discussion.

By the time of Eugene's visit, Cynthia had been on the phone to the Pallas Athene of Thrumborough; and although Mrs. Chancellor had clearly hoped against hope that her young friend would accept the inevitable and shut up, she was dutifully playing out the act. An appointment had been arranged for Cynthia and me to wait upon Mrs. C. at her house, the change of venue being due to Mrs. Chancellor's having caught cold. (I had asked to go along, thinking that if Cynthia were accompanied by someone older and not related to Great-aunt Persis, it would be harder to brush her off.)

Harry's cousin Eugene was in Europe when Harry testified in the *cause célèbre,* so we do not know what stand he would have taken then. This evening, when he heard about the withdrawal of Great-aunt Persis's invitation, he was shocked to the marrow; but when he learned that Cynthia and I were not going just to let the matter drop, he protested.

"Of course, it's horrible, Helen," he said warmly. "It makes me sick. It would make anyone sick. But be realistic about it."

This did not sound like the prelude to a clarion call such as Pericles' Funeral Oration—or even Kipling's *If*—but I wanted to see what Eugene's attitude would be, so I tried to look receptive.

"Why go to see Mrs. Chancellor again?" he said. "The lecture was going to be nothing but a nuisance for Cynthia's great-aunt. She'll be glad not to have to do it."

"Maybe," Harry replied, "if the building had burned down. But not on these terms."

Eugene's face showed that he appreciated the point. However, he persisted.

"I think you should drop the matter right here," he said. "It's the only dignified thing to do."

"Oh, Eugene!" I remonstrated mildly. "The Legion calls Great-aunt Persis a traitor or a bad influence or something, and everybody *appears* to agree! That isn't dignified."

Eugene looked distressed.

"I know," he said. "I know. But it isn't as simple as you think."

He got out cigarettes, and while he selected one and lit it, I had time to realize that he was identifying with Mrs. Chancellor in this situation, and not with Great-aunt Persis or Cynthia.

"For instance," Eugene said, and paused.

"There's another angle."

I waited.

"If you get yourself known as a crusader and a do-gooder about this, then when something really big comes along, you'll be automatically discounted."

I had thought of the point myself. It was one of the things that came to mind when I was lying in bed in the dark and could not get to sleep. But I had not been thinking of it very long when an answer suggested itself, and I gave the answer to Eugene.

"Nothing big is going to come along," I said. "Cynthia and I can't do anything about Apartheid. We're suburban housewives."

"If Helen doesn't get in the Legion's black book now," Harry said, "she may never make it."

Eugene laughed.

"Besides," I said, "this is big to Cynthia and me. It's not only big, it's monstrous."

"I'm not out of sympathy," Eugene said quickly, and added with some urgency, "you know that."

He smiled.

"Look," he said, "you're dragging me into this argument . . . But it's a matter of proportion."

I noticed Harry's quick scowl.

"Cynthia's great-aunt," Eugene continued, "is a terrifically wise and experienced woman. What is this going to mean to her?"

He answered his own question.

"A momentary flash of anger. An instant's twinge of annoyance and contempt."

"Oh, please!" I jumped from my chair. "This isn't television. Cynthia's great-aunt isn't just Claudette Colbert in a grey wig."

I drew breath.

"She's a real person."

Before Eugene could answer, I went on.

"Somewhere in one of her books, Mrs. Roosevelt says that you never get used to the lies and calumnies. You learn to live with them because you must, but they never cease to shock and outrage."

Although Eugene was clearly impressed, he frowned in a slightly puzzled way.

"But Great-aunt Persis," he said, apparently unaware that he had used the familial form of address, "has seen millions of Chinese dying of famine."

Harry leaned back in his chair.

"That will be a great comfort," he said.

Eugene flinched.

"You know that isn't . . ." he began hotly, and I quailed, expecting a family quarrel.

But Eugene took a deep breath and rammed his hands into his pockets.

"Cousin," he said reproachfully, "you have the tongue of an adder."

Harry looked at once regretful and not regretful, if that is possible, and I inspected Eugene carefully and decided he was at least half won over.

"Besides," I said, "it isn't just Great-aunt Persis. It's us they're humiliating, too."

Eugene gave a long, deep sigh.

"And people take you," I said, "at whatever value you let them put on you."

Harry's cousin capitulated.

"Yes," he agreed wholeheartedly, "that's true enough.

"It was really caddish," he supplied a moment later. "To trade on Cynthia's relationship to a famous woman. To exploit her willingness to help. And then . . ."

He turned to me.

"Nevertheless," he said—and was there the most infinitesimal bit of satisfaction in his tone? I could not tell—"I don't think you're going to persuade Mrs. Chancellor to resign."

"We can try."

The cousin's glance, as he looked at me, was interested and speculative.

"What will you do if she's adamant? If she just leaves Cynthia holding the bag?"

"Have her shanghaied," I returned promptly. "Taken to a waterfront dive and drugged. When she comes to, she'll find an American flag tattooed on her arm."

I hugged my elbows.

"That will keep her off the dais at hundred-dollar-a-plate dinners."

Eugene laughed. Looking at Harry, he said, "Maybe we really need a woman for President of the United States."

"Heaven forbid," I replied devoutly. "It would be too likely to be Mrs. Chancellor."

This gaiety of outlook, however, did not last long.

Pleased though I was that we had apparently engaged Eugene's sympathies—since it seemed to indicate that it was at least humanly possible to convey what we felt—I nevertheless got very little sleep the night before our call upon Mrs. Chancellor, and Friend Cynthia only slept after taking a pill.

"I feel ravaged," I said to Cynthia, as we drove toward Thrumborough, "and we haven't even seen her yet."

But as soon as we got into Mrs. Chancellor's living room, I felt that the house itself, at any rate, was on our side.

Mrs. Chancellor's living room does not actually have an embroidered bell pull hanging on the wall next to the fireplace, but it has pukka-sahib height and Widow-of-Windsor gloom. A few relatively modern chairs and lamps have been superimposed on the milieu of dark woodwork and Victorian clutter, but they do nothing to subtract from the impression that here is a place where the proprieties are going to be observed.

"We inherited the house from Brock's parents," Mrs. Chancellor said (obviously for the ten thousandth time) "and he never wanted to change it much."

Given this background, I did not have to look to see whether Mrs. Chancellor actually had a cold. I knew the forget-me-not eyes would be red-rimmed and a little rheumy, and they were.

No sooner were we seated than a maid brought in coffee —it was eleven o'clock in the morning—and as Mrs. Chancellor poured, she said effulgently to Cynthia, "I've had the most splendid idea. I want to give a lunch for your aunt."

Both Cynthia and I stiffened, and as Mrs. C. is not a seasoned administratrix for nothing, she got it at once.

"Cream?" she asked, and the subject was allowed to lapse.

I sipped my coffee. It was weak, but when a woman has Mrs. Chancellor's I-can-handle-hack-politicians demeanor, you may count yourself lucky if the brews from her kitchen do not taste of silver polish. That they should have flavor is expecting too much.

Cynthia swallowed some coffee and embarked on the suggestion that we had come to make. She led up to it, I thought, with just the right amount of deliberateness; managed to imply delicately that Mrs. Chancellor was no doubt herself thinking of resigning; alluded to the unimportance of the Women's Liberal Club in Mrs. C.'s agenda; and in general painted an inviting picture of an issue nobly faced.

It is harder to read the faces of people with colds than of people without, but as I observed Mrs. Chancellor's studious and attentive calm, I noticed a minute alteration that even the puffy tissue did not quite conceal.

"Ah," I thought to myself. "The simulated calm has become real calm. She's thought of the answer."

When Cynthia had finished, Mrs. Chancellor spoke with quiet simplicity.

"My children," she said. "I have to think of my children."

Cynthia and I awaited enlightenment.

"You're quite right that the Liberal Club isn't the closest to my heart of the things I do. But—"

Our hostess waved her hand in a gesture which seemed to invoke the whole neighborhood.

"—I live here."

She appealed for understanding.

"If I hurl defiance—" she smiled— "at the women on the Executive Committee . . . well . . . my children go to dances with their children."

Mrs. Chancellor looked at Cynthia, clearly expecting a ready understanding, but Cynthia's face was inscrutable.

"I haven't the right," Mrs. Chancellor concluded comfortably, "to make things difficult for my boy and girl."

"What would happen?" asked Cynthia.

The older woman frowned, but her voice was not impatient when she replied.

"Who can say? Being left out of things. Hearing unpleasant or hostile remarks."

Turning to me, she added, "As Shakespeare says, they're hostages to fortune."

"I should think," Cynthia said—and the expression on her face suddenly reminded me that she is the mother of the stubbornest little boy in the Western Republic—"that they'd admire you for standing up for your principles."

"Oh, my dear!" exclaimed Mrs. Chancellor quickly. "They're young!"

Not until after she had spoken did the implication of Cynthia's remark get home to her. Then, with a burst of anger, she said, "I'm a suspicious enough character as it is, with all the things I work for!"

But the mention of principles seemed to remind her of something, and with good humor apparently restored, she leaned toward Cynthia.

"My dear," she said sympathetically, "I know what's on your mind. I don't expect *you* to write to your aunt . . ."

As if it were literally before my eyes, I could see the letter that Mrs. Chancellor would write to Great-aunt Persis. Extravagantly regretful. Perhaps here and there even a little arch. The petrified turbulence of a meringue blanketing the curdled, watery custard underneath.

And this, I realized clearly, was as far as Mrs. C. was prepared to go in upholding the decorum evoked by her place of residence.

I had no time, however, to assess my painful emotions before I became aware that Mrs. Chancellor had turned away from Cynthia and was addressing herself to me.

"This is all so—well—so personal," she said. "The head of the Thrumborough Post of the Legion is really a very nice man."

Cynthia and I stared.

Mrs. Chancellor ignored our reaction, save for an almost mischievous toss of the head as she added with a smile, "I like him very much."

"My aunt," said Cynthia, "is a very nice woman."

Our hostess pretended not to have heard, but she began to sound more clogged up, as if her cold were getting worse.

"There are some really evil reactionaries around here," she said, "but Jim Afterbirth isn't one of them."

(This was not, presumably, the Legion head's name; but that was certainly the way it struck the ear.)

Our hostess pointed out through a tall window swathed in dark brocade to where the corner of a white house was just visible.

"He lives right over there," she said.

Turning briefly to Cynthia, she went on, "He knows who your aunt is, and he thinks she's practically another Dr. Schweitzer."

She swung back to me.

"Jim is just sick about this. He said to me, 'Maida, if it could only have happened next year, after my term expires.'"

"Then why . . . ?" I began.

"It's the national headquarters. They send out a list, and whenever anyone on this list is scheduled to speak in a tax-supported building, the local Post is supposed to try to stop it. Jim doesn't—"

"Oh," I said. "Cat on a cold tin roof."

Cynthia, I saw, was immobile with shock. I was brought up in an unhappy marriage—an unbroken home, I always call it—so I knew by the time I was a young woman that hatred itself can become routinized, and that people can go on being mechanically hurtful and automatically destructive long after the original impulse has spent itself. Cynthia, however, was just discovering this grimy truth.

"It's the last dying gasp of McCarthyism," pleaded Mrs. Chancellor.

Cynthia, obeying my glance, stood up.

Mrs. Chancellor whisked to a table, picked up a piece of paper and put it into my hand. It had, I saw, Great-aunt Persis's name at the top. The printing was in smudgy purple ink, and the two phrases that leaped out at me were "blasting *Counter-attack*" and "persons affiliated with 1-10 Communist-front organizations."

I heard Mrs. Chancellor saying something.

". . . from the records of the Senate Internal Security Sub-Committee," she concluded, with a brief return to the authority of people who can rattle off that sort of name.

But immediately she was the suppliant victor again, the apologetic conquistador.

"Naturally, everyone knows there's nothing in it."

She spoke, however, to empty space.

I had let the paper flutter to the seat of the nearest chair—it was a small, tufted sofa—and Cynthia and I were on our way out through the door.

P.S. I have set this down more than two weeks after the event, but the sense of decencies violated and proprieties flouted does not wear off. Oddly enough, both Cynthia and I have an overwhelming reluctance to commit any part of this situation to writing. Cynthia has not yet written to her great-aunt, and I know—although she has not put it into exactly these words—it is because of her feeling that merely to transmit this rejection is in a way to be identified with the people who have done it.

Cynthia feels particularly bitter that her Neighbor-ladies, who were all nods and becks and wreathèd smiles when Great-aunt Persis was written up in *Time,* accepted the subsequent development with perfect equanimity. A shrug, a rueful little moue, and they turned to other things. I myself would have expected at least a slight measure of confusion in the Neighborladies. *Time,* which is an authority, declared Great-aunt Persis good. Then the Legion, which is also an authority, declared her bad. But the Neighborladies take their cue from whichever au-thority happened to speak to them last.

Life goes on, of course. One shells the peas. (The Fitzgibbonses have reached—temporarily, at any rate—a state of total boredom with the uniform perfection of frozen vegetables.) The weather has been flawless, with only enough rain to keep the green things from getting parched, and June sails into the future like a trireme across the Aegean. But one is haunted; and not, unfortunately, by the Ghost of Christmas Past.

June 23rd ✑ Our cats have not read the literature in which they could learn, if they wished, that they are aloof, independent and haughtily indifferent to the human be-ings who take care of them. Hence they also do not know that Harry and I, as cat-owners, are demonstrably stronger of character and tougher of intellect than people who need the coarse, rank flattery and chin-on-paws devotion of a dog to soothe their egos.

The foregoing may be stereotypes, but Harry and I have always thought them more interesting and less banal than most such generalizations. Young Cat and Old Cat, however—or perhaps all Siamese?—seem to take a perverse pleasure in reducing the stereotypes to mincemeat. This afternoon I came home from the public library (modeled on Faneuil Hall, and located just where Hotdogwagonstrasse meets Auto Parts Boulevard) with a promising harvest. When I took my books and a glass of iced tea out to the porch, Young Cat was asleep on the couch, and he should by all proper standards merely have opened one eye and closed it again.

If that.

Instead, he leaped to his feet and thence to the floor, and eyed me alertly. When I was settled into my chair, he sat down on the floor in front of me, looking eloquently up into my face and purring so hard that he throbbed all over like an excursion steamer backing water.

Just as I began to drink my tea, he jumped into my lap, thereby sprinkling a little ice-cold beverage on both of us. Not even pausing to lick it off, he thrust his nose into the slight opening between my sweater and my blouse. Blocked by an immobile elbow, he withdrew and reared up to place a chocolate-colored paw with consummate delicacy on the brooch at my throat.

Satisfied that I was still every inch my delicious and intoxicating self, he turned around twice and curled up in my lap with his head facing me.

"Who are you?" I said coldly. "A refugee from the American Kennel Club?"

(I, at least, was aware that a cherished reputation for objectivity hung trembling in the balance.)

Larkspur, sapphire, the robes of a Memling Madonna are not bluer than the eyes he turned up to my face.

"I *love* you!" he said.

June 24th ~~ Some days when you go out, you seem to
see an unusual number of lame people or blind men; and
similarly in some weeks a particular word or phrase will
turn up in almost every newspaper or magazine you put
your hand to. This week the word "other-directed" has
leaped out at me from everything up to and including the
recipes for summer squash on the woman's page. Seeing it
so much has given me the quaint notion that, strictly
speaking, the phrase is not entirely accurate.

When all those hundreds of thousands of American
tourists go to Europe every summer, they do not say, "We
must be careful of the feelings of the Italians"—

"We must not affront the notions of the French"—

"We must not cause dismay among the British"—

"We must make the Swedes feel that we are all part of
a team"—

If Americans entertained sentiments like that, they
would be *really* other-directed. What the sociologists
mean is not "other-directed," but "similar-directed."

June 25th ~~ How close beneath the surface, even in
the happiest family, is the chronic grievance! I sometimes
think that tinderboxes are inert and powder kegs mere
talcum compared to the explosive possibilities in the most
commonplace domestic situation.

Last evening, after dinner, Cora and Harry slouched
furtively off—I did not see them, but I know that is how
they looked—to play softball on the little flat place at the
top of the hill where the local Shropshire Lads (and their
children) often gather on a summer evening. This de-

fection left the Mater Dolorosa all alone to do the dishes, change the cats' pans and put gallon after gallon of water on some evergreens we have just transplanted.

The eloquence with which I arraigned the defaulters in my mind, as I slammed the dishes into the drainer—it turned out to be more difficult to slam a two-and-a-half-gallon watering can—was worthy of a William Jennings Bryan.

"You shall not press down upon the brow of Mother this crown of thorns!"

"You are selfish, inconsiderate and devoted to nothing but your own crude pleasures!"

"I'm nothing but an unpaid servant around here!"

"Day in and day out, I put up with the grotesqueries of Plethora . . ."

"Alone and desolate in the midst of twenty-five square miles of Neighborladies . . . (Well, all right, there's Cynthia, but she's younger) . . ."

Fortunately, the truants came back before these heady phrases had grown limp with overuse, and I spoke to my loved ones without niggling inhibitions or paralyzing restraints. Cora, flushed with the triumph of softball and Harry's company, elected to be impudent. Peering out from what she imagined to be a safe coign of vantage behind the paternal legs, she remarked pertly, "You don't have to do all that work. Nobody asked you to."

I swooped.

A good sharp slap on the rear end, suspension of the weekly allowance for a month, and immediate retirement to bed though it lacked ten minutes of the time were among the least of the correctives I planned for her.

I would break her to private.

I would send her back to pounding a beat.

But Harry laid a hand on my arm.

"You treat us," he said reproachfully, "as if we were opposed to changing the cats' pans *in principle*. But we're really awfully nice chaps, and we're only opposed to it in practice."

June 28th ～ I paid a visit this afternoon to a former neighbor whose husband has bettered himself by geometric rather than by arithmetic progression and who now lives in a sort of pocket version of a Stately Home of England. The house is in a neighborhood where people protect the evergreens all winter with burlap tents. (Or, rather, their gardeners do.) This seems to me to defeat the whole purpose of having evergreens; and the supererogatory burlap started me reflecting on the American mania for putting covers on things.

We put plastic covers on toasters, electric mixers, nests of bowls, and the very piles of plates in the dish closet; covers on the seats of cars, rainproof covers on the garden furniture, elasticized covers on the living-room chairs, covers in the summer on the lamp shades and curtains, fuzzy covers on the toilet seats and covers on the clothes hanging in the closet. At least, we do if one can believe the advertisements in the Sunday papers; and those fellows do not usually wanton about with products that stay sluggishly on the shelf.

Is it possible that, despite all the talk about space conquest, nose cones and galaxies, we have never really gotten the antimacassar and the tea cozy out of our blood?

I was driving sedately home, thinking these thoughts, when a car full of young boys, some of them holding tilted, foaming beer cans out of the window, came tearing past a STOP sign and hurtled right into my path. My brakes screamed humanly as I automatically flung out an arm to keep Cora from going through the windshield, although she did not happen to be with me at the time. I had an infinitesimal glimpse of backward-turned, laughing faces, and then the murderous conveyance was only a pinpoint at the end of the street.

Whenever I see young people driving like that, I always (after, of course, the first homicidal retaliatory impulse) want to put them on a horse. If, I think to myself, they can manage one of those surly brutes whose forefeet never touch the ground and whose mouths are as sensitive to pressure as Mammoth Cave, then I do not mind their driving at seventy miles an hour in a residential district. But one wants one's swashbucklers validated. One wants to see them handle something that fights back.

July 3rd ❧ I wish I could somehow catch and preserve forever the way in which Cora, in bed and ready to be kissed good night, summons her parents by calling, "Come up!"

On this occasion, wishing to be heard, she speaks with great distinctness; and the balance between the confident imperiousness of the command and the extremely light timbre of the voice has something almost Mozartian about it.

There is something of Wolfgang Amadeus, too, about the conversations we have on these occasions.

Could you, Cora asks, call a room in which you are healthy a firmary?

Or she remarks that honeysuckle blossoms are shaped exactly like quotation marks—which, upon observation, they proved to be. (It gives me a mental picture of hummingbirds in frozen flight over a page of dialogue.)

Cora had two friends to supper tonight, and I was amused to note that although there is a wide French door opening onto the porch, all three children, when summoned to the evening meal, casually and matter-of-factly climbed through the living-room window. For a minute, I had a pang of purest envy, wishing I still had the kind of muscles that respond automatically to the challenge of a window sill. Alas, I am so far along in life that a window sill is not even, any more, a thing on which to lean while being serenaded. It has become merely a surface to dust.

July 5th ❧ "The rainy Pleiads wester," the poet lyrically says—but neglects to add that after five days of uninterrupted bad weather, the flagged stone floor of the porch sweats, and people wearing sneakers skid on it. Upstairs and down, we are encircled and enshrouded by wet leaves, so that even when it is not actually raining—which is seldom—there is the sound of splash and drip. Beyond the porch a large elm-tree branch, slanting diagonally almost to the ground, moves mournfully hither and yon in the moist air, creating the effect of a bush-league Wuthering Heights.

Considered as a holiday, the Glorious Fourth could have gratified no one but the late Major André. However, the Fitzgibbonses are hoping that this is the storm before the lull, for we leave for the farm in three days.

July 7th ❧ I would not go so far as to say that Mrs. Brock Chancellor has left a trail of carnage behind her. It is rather that she stains the white radiance of eternity like one of those dingy films the toothpaste commercials are always talking about.

Cynthia is God's Angry Woman about it all. For my own part, I suffer the discomfort of a slightly divided attitude. It is wonderful that Cynthia is sufficiently clear-sighted to see the recent happening for what it is—and spirited enough to resent it. On the other hand, there is no denying that Maida Chancellor has become Cynthia's King Charles's Head. Even Russ has occasionally said, "Steady the Buffs!" when Cynthia rekindled, although Russ is the patient Englishman if ever there was one.

Certainly, various little things have conspired to exacerbate Cynthia's feelings. She is as yet only tangentially involved with the Samuel T. Atkinson Grade School. Her older boy, the beautiful one, was in kindergarten this past year. Nevertheless, she generously—and in view of her arduous life, it was really generous—painted a cyclorama for an American history pageant that was mounted at Samuel T. Atkinson the day before school closed.

Cora, clad in apron and fichu and looking about as sturdy as a light-bulb filament, was a Pioneer Woman in a log-cabin-and-square-dance sequence, so both Cynthia and I attended the performance. By ill luck, the teacher who wrote the pageant concluded it with some orotundities, spoken by a fifth-grader, on freedom of speech. In this bit of rhetoric, freedom of speech was referred to, not as a goal to be worked for, but as one already achieved and requiring only the amount of effort that goes into hearty self-congratulation. To listen to the Samuel T. Atkinson infant piping down the valleys wild—to be forcibly reminded of Great-aunt Persis's luminous achievements and Mrs. Chancellor's children going to dances—was an embittering experience for me and well nigh intolerable for Cynthia.

And on a later occasion, when Cynthia and I were sitting on her porch, Cora came over to ask if I would phone one of her friends, with whom she had promised to "sleep over," and break the engagement. She had a better invitation. Cynthia and I—as I talked to Cora about the importance of living up to obligations—could scarcely avoid making the sardonic mental reference to Thrumborough and the Executive Committee of the Women's Liberal Club.

Cynthia has not yet written to Great-aunt Persis, and we assume that Mrs. Chancellor has not steeled herself to the unseductive task, either. At any rate, there has been no word from India to indicate that Cynthia's distinguished relative has been apprised of her fate.

July 10th ✺ The Wake-Robin Farm.

Well, I scarcely know what to say.

But perhaps one really ought to begin at the beginning.

Since the journey here was four hundred miles long, we broke it by staying overnight at a motel. The pre-motel hours of the trip were largely marked by jangling family tension. For one thing, it was scorchingly hot. Cora started the hegira neatly and obligingly by going to sleep on the back seat. But she woke up all too soon; and in what seemed like no time whatsoever, she had run through the minute (according to her) collection of games brought along for her amusement. After that, she started in on that Pilgrims' Chorus which is even more familiar, if less majestic, than the one in *Tannhäuser:* "How long before we get there?"

It was hot! And Harry and I were not spellbound with admiration for each other's driving. Disunity reached a point, in fact, where we even resorted to that corny and ignoble gambit, the haughtily elevated profile.

And to remarks such as "I wouldn't say anything, except that good heavens! we've got to stay alive."

"I suppose," snapped Harry at one point, "you're going to remind me that we have a Precious Cargo on the back seat."

As that very admonition—save for the Precious Cargo locution—had been trembling on my lips, I was silenced.

But not soothed.

"I know what *you* need," I said, after a pause.

"What?" asked Harry grudgingly, but clearly expecting an olive-branch reply like "A cold glass of beer" or "A clean restroom."

"A marriage counselor," I said.

"Mommy!" said the Precious Cargo. "How long before we get there?"

Since we did not have to rush, Harry had mapped out a route which took us to our destination by secondary roads. I remember reading in one of Cynthia's design textbooks that lines dominate the area to which they are adjacent; and certainly the thruways and turnpikes "control" (in the artistic sense) the earth immediately around them. Even when there are no billboards and the restaurants are uniform and widely spaced, the American super-highway throws off a sort of prow wave of sterility through which it rides like a motorboat.

Because of the secondary roads, we had all three formed a mental picture of ourselves stopping in some cool and shady grove or on some hilltop of nodding grasses to eat the lunch we had brought along. But we had reckoned without our compatriots. Every bit of woodland, every pastoral expanse, that looked wonderful as we approached turned out on closer inspection to be a kitchen midden of beer cans, Lily cups, cigarette packages, chewing gum wrappers and paper bags that had had commercial cookies in them.

At first, we were all three united in our disappointment. But when we drove away from the sixth town dump in a row that had been thinly disguised with maple trees, a difference of opinion developed. As I got hungrier and hungrier, it began to seem to me more and more imperative not to eat until we could find some place where the repast could really be enjoyed. Harry and Cora, on the other hand, were increasingly willing to settle for what they could get, and as they outnumbered me, we soon stopped in a pretty spot with the usual litter.

The others applied themselves heartily to the viands, but I ate half a sandwich and then sat erect, with hands folded, on the blanket we had spread—Whistler's Sister, at the very least.

"Human nature is human nature," Harry said, with cheerful didacticism. (The intake of food and of a couple of glasses of chilled white wine had disposed him to take a brighter view of things.)

"The Acropolis at the height of its fame," he said, "was a shambles of gawdy statues and junk-filled peristyles."

Though startled by the information, which was new to me, I exercised great self-control and merely turned my head away in a manner which I thought none the less sorrowful and dignified for having been copied from Jack Benny.

However, within twenty minutes of our being on the road again, I was constrained by the pangs of hunger to ask for a hot sandwich and a hot apple from the shelf behind the back seat, and after that we all relaxed a little. By this time, we had come into nobly rolling country which seemed to be a combination of farmland and resort area. Most of the farms were away in the middle distance, but one or two that we saw close up were rather alarmingly miry as to dooryard.

Harry and I, nevertheless, decided by tacit agreement not to cross any bridges till we came to them; and after another couple of hours of driving, we started looking for a motel. Or, rather, we started trying to select one, since at some parts of the road there were so many of these welcoming and open-armed caravansaries that one would have had difficulty putting down a sleeping bag between them. When we finally picked one out and checked in, I was recalled to my own childhood by Cora's reactions.

My early years were moveless and stationary, as was usual in those days, but once I was taken to stay overnight in a hotel in Newport, Rhode Island, and never in all the time since has my instinct for elegance been so totally satisfied. What did it matter that the porcelain in the spacious bathroom was faintly rust-stained or that there were worn spots in the red staircase carpet? I ignored such irrelevancies. This was Splendor.

I thought of that experience when I saw Cora opening the dressing-table drawers, bouncing on the beds and trying out the drawstrings of the window curtains. Our accommodations in the motel had a paper mat to protect one's feet from the bathroom floor, lyre-shaped pieces of paper to protect the gluteus maximus from the toilet seat, and a paper jacket to protect the bathroom glass from the touch of any unhallowed lip. Nevertheless, the room smelled faintly of raw lumber, and the nylon curtains lacked the voluptuous swell and fall which make Sir Joshua Reynolds' backgrounds so impressive.

To Cora, however, it was pure Reynolds. As she plunged out the door—in order to peer through the window "and see how we look from out there"—Harry turned to me with raised, inquiring eyebrow.

"It's Not-Home," I said. "It's Otherwhere."

We ate dinner in a restaurant down the road. The food suggested that the American passion for foam rubber has perhaps been carried a bit too far; but any piece of lettuce which I have not myself bought, washed and put on the table—and whose oily remains I do not have to shovel into a step-on garbage pail—is to me a transcendently beautiful piece of lettuce. As Cora dropped off to sleep on a couch in a corner of the motel room, and I got into bed and opened up *The Last Chronicle of Barset*, I reflected that I, too, am still susceptible to the charms of Otherwhere.

Here endeth the first day.

We got up yesterday morning in an atmosphere of unaccustomed leisure and took our time about packing and getting on the road again. Breakfast was eaten when we had been under way for about half an hour, and we partook of it in a modest establishment where the proprietress was cheerful and obliging and a black-and-white cat responded with good-natured condescension to being made much of by Cora and me.

The weather was glorious, and less hot than yesterday. After a while we realized that we had left the summer resorts behind and were running through what seemed to be largely grazing country. When we came over the crests of hills, there would be only about four farmhouses in sight (with the inevitable clustered trees and red or grey barn) from horizon to horizon. The cow population was abundant, however, and the landscape redolent of peace and plenty. Nevertheless, Harry and I began to feel a scary sensation. What would the farm be like? What could you expect for so small a sum as thirty dollars a week? Would there be other people staying there? If so, what sort of people?

We had lunch at a drugstore in a small town and it seemed funny to be eating ice cream that tasted of talcum powder after having driven all morning through a sea of udders. But we were getting close to our destination, and that was our main preoccupation.

Following the admirably clear directions given us by Miriam Brown, the farmer's wife, we eventually turned off the macadam into a network of gravelly thoroughfares that took us deeper and deeper into the undisturbed quiet of the country. Fields of corn stood motionless on either side of the roads. Swallows perched on the telephone wires. At last we took one turn and then another—the second one observed impassively by a sway-backed white horse—and came to what could only have been Wake-Robin Farm.

Harry stopped the car and pulled up the brake.

We looked.

The photograph had not lied. It was a strongly proportioned house, with cupola. Set on a little slope, it had trees—big, patriarchal maples, ash and a few oaks—protecting it in the back and on one side. The two halves of the double front door were arched, and through them one could see a straight and arrowy stairway rising to considerable height in the front hall.

But the wire mesh of the screen door had come almost completely off the frame and was hanging by a thread. The house had once been painted white, but no paintbrush seemed to have touched it for a good fifteen years. The front steps sagged. In the lattice which supposedly screened the area under the porch were several large holes. The house ran out in a sort of ell at one side, and the porch followed its contours. At the far end of the porch stood a washing machine of design so antique as to be palpably unusable, and near it washing hung from lines strung up near the roof.

Properly speaking, there was no lawn. The ground merely erupted into coarse tufts of growth, and scattered about on this unappealing vegetation were an express wagon, a kiddie car and some dolls and children's toys that had seen much wear and tear. The driveway ran from the road past one side of the house and around to the back. At the bottom, near the road, it was a buffalo wallow; but halfway up the slope it turned abruptly into a kind of rock-strewn Negev. Beyond it, under the trees, a collection of rusty machinery stood unprotected from the weather.

For a minute, both Harry and I were silent and stunned. Then I turned to him.

"Excuse me for just one minute," I said, "while I step out to the plowed furrows and bear this child."

Harry gave an abrupt laugh and reached toward the

ignition. I did not have to ask what we were going to do. We were going to the nearest town and telephone some excuse—any excuse—that would spare us the amenities of this domestic Andersonville.

But just at that moment a young girl came running down the driveway. She wore blue jeans and I deduced that she must be the twelve-year-old, Rayleine. Coming unhesitantly up to the car, she said with a completely natural warmth, "You must be the Fitzgibbonses. Did you bring your little girl?"

I reached for the door handle.

"Yes," I said, preparing to get out. "We're all here."

Rayleine seemed to be in complete charge. Nobody else appeared, and when Harry had unloaded the bags, we went indoors. To my inordinate relief, the interior gave the impression of being more orderly and clean than the outside. Rayleine guided us up the heaven-breaching staircase to a bedroom that would have seemed large, save that it had two double beds in it. There was linoleum on the floor, an armoire for clothes, a straight chair, a night table with a very Woolworth-ish lamp and a dresser which looked as if the weight of a pair of sunglasses would cause it to buckle. The two large windows had paper curtains and framed a beautiful, farming-country view which was perfectly accented by a stand of dark pines.

Harry put down the suitcases; and when we had finished looking around and taking our bearings, we saw that Cora and Rayleine had quietly disappeared. Left to ourselves in the silent house, we explored. The bathroom down the hall was large but windowless. Obviously, it had been made by cutting off a piece from one of the bedrooms.

We went downstairs to the living room. What struck me instantly about the living room was that the furniture —the room was large and held two "suites" of sofa and matching chairs—was not just shabby. It was worn down to the nub. Though somewhat darkened by the porch, the room had two bay windows with Boston ferns growing vigorously in each. There were also a television set, a table with pictures of the Browns' children which showed that the older boy was married, and a small bookcase with titles like *Maid of Old Provence, A Prairie Wife, Santa Fé Sweetheart* and other sedate forerunners of *Peyton Place* and tingly John O'Hara.

Behind the living room, we could see a dining room— also with bay window, and accommodating an enormous table. There were several tall doors opening off the din- ing room, but it seemed indelicate to crash into the pene- tralia uninvited, so Harry and I went outside.

If I had rejoiced briefly that the house appeared to be clean, that cup was soon dashed from my lips. At the kitchen door were what had started out as several ordinary corrugated iron garbage barrels, but they had been so inundated by used tin cans as to form a sort of sprawling metal pyre about four feet high, and over this tumulus buzzed and hovered and swarmed a curtain of flies.

Instinctively, I recoiled.

In the milieu in which I was brought up, the one over- weening peril to all health and well-being was Germs.

And who carried Germs?

Flies carried Germs, that's who!

My first feeling about unself-conscious Rayleine had been that I would be strung up by the thumbs before I would let her realize that I thought there was anything wrong with her house. But when I discovered Rayleine's mother operating a sort of Ford Foundation for the insect world, my own altruism was gone in a flash. Mentally, I had already reloaded the car, driven four hundred miles and was back at home when I saw a movement inside the house and a voice called us to come in.

We entered a big kitchen, where an old coal range— now obviously superseded by the gas range next to it— was piled with boxes of dry cereal, cans of spaghetti and piles of toilet paper and soap. Across the room, an oval table with a figured plastic cloth had six chairs around it. The punched leather seat of one of the chairs was almost entirely torn out and hanging down, so there was not much to sit on but the rim. Nevertheless, the room had a kind of neatness, in a cluttered way, and the summer breeze and summer sunshine poured into it pleasurably.

Beyond the kitchen, in a big, old-fashioned pantry with tall closets, Mrs. Brown was slicing tomatoes. She said "Hello" matter-of-factly and went on with her job. By asking, we learned that we were the only visitors at the moment, but that more people were expected next day. We also learned that we could get to the swimming place by taking a path which started out behind the house and went off over the hill.

Curiously enough, Mrs. Brown had the same effect on me as her daughter Rayleine had had. I looked forward to being the stranger within these gates as I would to spending a week in a septic tank, but not for worlds did I want Mrs. Brown to know it.

Leaving the kitchen and pausing by the Ford Foundation, we were confronted with two paths. A short one to the right was lined with discarded tires, broken machinery, weeds and mammoth sunflowers. It ended in a paintless board fence upon which Rayleine and Cora were companionably draped, and from behind which came the sound of pigs. The other path led up over the hill, apparently to the swimming place.

As the kitchen screen door—whose protective mesh was also waving slackly in the air—creaked behind us, Cora turned to her parents the face of one whose dreams have all come true.

"The barn," she said.

It was directly ahead of us, built into the side of the hill, and we went in through a small side door. Within lay perfection—the Rembrandt lighting, the smell of hay, the vastness. No further explanation was needed for the Lassie-came-home expression on Cora's face—or for Mrs. Brown's assurance in her letter that they never had any trouble keeping the children amused.

Leaving the barn, Harry and I set off to look for the swimming place. A pleasant walk led to it—a walk compounded of hill, breeze, cowpats, noise of insects, big sky, distant herds and humble flowers like Queen Anne's Lace, yarrow and butter-and-eggs. The tiny lake itself, however, was unimpressive. Marshy at the edges and not sparkling in the middle, it had the sodden look of a bowl of cornflakes which has been left standing on the table all morning. Nor was it much bigger.

"The carp pond is a dud," said Harry. "Let's get back to the Establishment."

When we re-entered the barnyard, Cora was talking to a man in blue jeans whose face had the human and crumbly quality of a typewriter erasure. He introduced himself as Clarence Brown. Farmer Brown was the first member of the family to display the slightest touch of the professional welcomer. He was by no means a cruise director; but that kindly, rugged face, one felt, had had a great success with city people and its owner was aware of the fact. Just the same, there was genuineness in the invitation which he and Cora both extended to come and watch the milking when the cows came in.

Harry and I, a little wearied by new sensations, retired to our room to unpack, rest and write a few letters saying that there were rather more mosses on the old manse than anticipated, but that Cora was finding it an earthly Paradise and we thought we could stick it for a week.

We were half dozing when a reverberant moo announced the arrival of the cows. Going to the window, we saw about fifty of them moving compliantly into the barn under the direction of Cora and Rayleine.

The barn was on several levels, and the cows were milked on the lowest. The ground immediately outside was a morass of whose ingredients one did not like to think too closely, and Cora, like the cows, was mired to the hocks. But only a Nazi would have had the heart to intrude a remonstrance on her new-found pride of office. With a little switch she carried, our daughter flicked a cow on the bony pelvis; and when Bossy momentarily quickened her pace, it was evident even from our distance away that Cora was tasting the ineffable sweetness of authority.

The cow barn itself proved to have a cement floor, when we descended to it through the interior. Mr. Brown had been joined by the boys Fanshawe and Henderson, who were not bad-looking, though a little red of face and strawy of hair for the elegance of their names. The Browns were also assisted by a hired man for whose age, toothlessness and indifference to personal hygiene I had not been prepared by Squire Robert Frost.

Working in silence and with smooth, empty faces, the four men fastened animals into stalls, hooked milking machines to udders and emptied buckets of milk into the big forty-gallon cans. It was a picture of sustained activity, and yet one had to watch for only about two minutes to realize that the scene had a notably tranquilizing effect.

Perhaps it was the rows of rumps, the languidly switching tails and the distinctive, corny fragrance of cattle. Perhaps it was the dusky light, which seemed to emanate from the splattered, cobwebby, white walls rather than from the still-brilliant daylight outside. Perhaps it was the smoothly patterned motion of people at a task both totally familiar and totally inescapable. Or maybe it was merely the presence of the great primary source of food. Whatever it was, one was aware of pulse slowing down and urgencies melting away.

Harry felt it, too.

"What is the opposite," he asked, "of a sticky wicket?"

" 'A little bit of all right.' "

"This is it," he said.

Somebody had swung Cora up onto the back of a cow, and from this vantage point, she indicated a very pregnant animal and told us that it was going to drop its calf any day now.

Rayleine, in the presence of her family, had abandoned some of her grown-up air of responsibility. Scrambling up on one of the stalls, she demonstrated how well she could chin herself on the beam above. In the intervals of gymnastics, she imparted information. (If a certain glibness showed she had dispensed it often, she had still by no means lost her prideful zest for the job.)

Fanshawe, the married son, lived "over by the next pavement." Henderson lived during the summer in a little shack about a hundred yards down the road. The hired man drove over from some unexplained provenance and was, Rayleine said, not reliable. The Browns had bought the farm during the depression, and for the first ten years they never left the place except to buy supplies because there were no baby-sitters in those days.

Fanshawe and Henderson had won prize after prize in the 4-H Club, but the 4-H Club was no longer in existence because the very nice lady who ran it had died, and the government did not appoint anyone to take her place. Three calves which I noticed tied up in a miry, uncemented and completely dark corner of the barn were never let out into the daylight—why, I cannot remember. Their imprisonment struck me as pathetic and made me long for some writs of habeas corpus, but I was already beginning to sense that on a working farm it does not do to express too much poetic sensitivity about the feelings of animals.

Rayleine swung herself away hand over hand along the beam and dropped to earth, we knew not where. Cora had disappeared from the cow's back. Harry and I stayed and watched the milking till the last forty-gallon can had been wrestled into a sort of little ice house adjoining to await collection in the morning. Then, feeling completely at peace, we started back toward the house.

It may have been in part because I was so relaxed from watching the milking that the next incident had the impact on me that it did. The next incident was supper, and the uninvited guests at supper were the little jet pilots of contagion, the little wingèd sowers of disease, the Ford Foundation clients. One end of the dining-room table was set with four places, for Rayleine was to eat with us. Mrs. Brown and Vanessa had already had their meal. (Vanessa was a large, shy and slightly puffy adolescent who seemed, compared to the wiry and assured Rayleine, rather like a frightened marshmallow.) The men would eat later, when the chores were done.

As I approached the dining-room table, the first thing I saw was a large white pitcher of milk from which a fly was trying to extricate himself by doing the Australian crawl. Flies skated across the clean white plates. They perched on the edge of the butter dish. They sat on the bread and went through their characteristic gesture of spitting on the forepaws and then energetically shampooing the grisly brown head. Over each end of the table hung a long, sticky spiral of flypaper, and each spiral was generously dotted with corpses in positions indicating they had died game.

The food seemed to consist of packaged ham from a supermarket, potato salad, lettuce and tomatoes, canned peaches and Lorna Doones; but there was so much motion going on between me and the table that the victuals were not clearly observable.

"I can't!"

The cry rose imperiously in my overcharged bosom— so imperiously that I thought I had spoken it aloud. But although a human voice did break in on this scene of corruption and sepsis, it was Cora's and not mine.

Cora's black-lashed eyes were agreeably alight as she watched three dive bombers peel off from a flight formation and head for the Peenemunde of the sugar bowl.

"Look!" she said happily. "Airborne raisins."

For one dreadful moment I thought I was going to be a

victim of what the doctors call reverse peristolsis; but the cerebrum mercifully assumed command and slapped the vaulting stomach down.

I looked at Harry, and there was no doubt but what that doughty spirit was taken aback; and yet I could already see in his lineaments the dawn of resignation and acceptance. No corresponding dawn lit up my own psyche, and I lowered myself into my chair as if it had electrodes on it.

Nevertheless, I made an effort to see life steadily and see it whole.

"George Washington's dinner table," I reminded myself, "must have had just such a blanket of flies."

But so far from comforting me, this thought merely suggested that that would account for the grim look so often worn by the Father of His Country in the portraits.

By keeping my mind resolutely on other things, I managed to get down a little of the food, criss-crossed though it was, in my view, with invisible trails of contamination. Afterwards I found a piece of gum in my purse and, by chewing vigorously on that, made myself feel that I had eaten more than I actually had.

The evening meal concluded, Rayleine generously offered to read to Cora, so Harry and I took a walk along the utterly quiet, graveled road on which Wake-Robin Farm stands. A sickle of moon rode in the pure sky of the west, and along the edges of the road were only clover and tiger lilies—no beer cans or litter. We re-encountered the sway-backed white horse, who was a draft animal of mountainous proportions, and he came over to the fence and exhaled on us—but retreated hastily when I reached out my hand to pat his nose.

Looking around me, I said, "You can't have everything," and Harry nodded, knowing what I meant.

When we returned, I supervised Cora's bath and sat with her during the two minutes it took her to fall asleep. Then I went down to the living room and tried to read *The Last Chronicle of Barset.* By this time, the Browns had all disappeared into a wing they apparently occupied somewhere back of the kitchen. By this time, also, I was close to the whimpering point from pangs of unsatisfied hunger.

Finishing a chapter in *Barset,* I said pathetically to Harry, "All I want is a clean, modern place where I can get something good to eat."

"Poor darling," replied Harry compassionately, and returned to his reading.

We both knew that there was no recourse. The nearest town was a little hamlet about ten miles away—the kind of little hamlet where even the soldier on the Civil War monument seems to be saying, "Anyone don't eat t' hum, kin go hongry." Had I been poultry or pigs, the little town might have essayed to feed me, but the paying guests of Mrs. Clarence Brown it regarded as amply provided for.

Another chapter of *Barset* and I said to Harry, "You know for whom I'm developing a tremendous respect?"

"No," said Harry. "Who?"

"Whom?" he emended a minute later.

"Gandhi," I said. "To think he starved on purpose!"

Harry smiled in an automatic way—immersed in his book—and I recalled that, while fanning the air steadily with one hand, he had managed to put away a pretty good meal with the other.

I was only halfway through the next chapter of *Barset*

when I felt impelled to speak again—though aware that I did not have my audience on the edge of its seat.

"There's something about myself I've always wondered."

"Mm-m-m?"

"Whether my character would stand up under real strain."

Harry gave his head a little tilt to one side, to show that he was listening, even though he did not appear to be.

"And now I know it wouldn't."

There was no answer.

"Right now," I said, "there would be no betrayal too degrading for me to accede to, if rewarded by a toasted chicken sandwich."

At this provocative statement, Harry closed his book, stood up and left the room. But he was back in two minutes with a candy bar he had found in the glove compartment of the car. I have seen mosaics from Herculaneum and Pompeii that were in far better shape than that candy bar, but I snapped like a wolf at the senescent confection.

We went to bed immediately afterward, and I went happily to sleep with the taste of chocolate in my mouth. (I purposely did not clean my teeth. I did not wish to lose the extra nourishment.)

July 11th ✎ Such was our introduction to the sternly beautiful world of Willa Cather and the Dairymen's League.

I woke up at 6:15 yesterday morning with the trim and virtuous feeling of not having overeaten. Harry was still sound asleep, but Cora had already dressed and left. At least, she was not in the bathroom and her clothes were gone.

Leaning out of the window, I could not help but feel cheerful. The lawn around the house, to be sure, suggested a sort of horticultural psoriasis; but the surrounding fields glittered with dew, the sky was brilliant and cloudless, and the uncluttered agricultural landscape looked as if it were fresh from the easel of an Old Master.

I went down to the kitchen—"What a house for a wedding!" I thought as I descended the long front staircase—and learned from Mrs. Brown that Cora had had her breakfast and was out in the barn with Rayleine and the men. It was gratifying to realize that Cora was so much at home in this new environment that she did not need to wake her parents for instruction or companionship. It was almost equally gratifying to realize that it was still too early for the flies to be up and about.

Mrs. Brown invited me to eat with her in the kitchen, instead of alone in the dining room, so I poured myself a dish of dry cereal and was just about to sit down when I realized that I had appropriated the seatless chair. With a movement that was far from suggesting Anna Pavlova in *The Swan*, I switched at the last possible moment to a sounder piece of furniture. For a split second I wondered whether protocol required me to pretend there was nothing wrong with the first chair, but Miriam Brown was looking straight at me and did not seem to feel that any slur had been put upon the local Hepplewhite.

Mrs. Brown offered me eggs, but I declined, and when I saw her drop a couple into a frying pan so hot that the eggs jumped four inches out of the searing fat, I was glad not to have committed myself. Conversation with Miriam Brown introduced me—sketchily, at least—to a world different from mine. Clarence Brown loves to hunt and fish and he has a friend named Meller who lives, actually, in a suburb near ours. Mr. and Mrs. Meller—"They don't get along too well," Mrs. Brown said—were to arrive that very day, and one evening this week, Mr. Brown and Mr. Meller will leave after supper, drive all night to a fishing spot some hundreds of miles away, fish all day, and then drive back the following night. Mr. Brown will get here just in time for the morning milking and will then pick up and carry on with his usual day's work.

It must come from being outdoors so much.

Harry is some years younger than Clarence Brown, but I can hardly imagine his embarking on such a strenuous schedule except in an emergency.

The other *outré* item had to do with Rayleine's having, as a younger child, made a great fuss when having her teeth attended to. On one occasion the local dentist got so annoyed with her screams and tears that he rammed his hand, with a fistful of instruments in it, into the back of her mouth and kept it there until she started turning blue in the face. I, or any other suburban matron of my acquaintance, would first have beaten the man over the head with the calfskin purse and then have sued him from hell to breakfast for malpractice. But Mrs. Brown only remarked in a tone of mild regret that she was afraid the dentist was rather rough, and then added more cheerfully that after that, Rayleine had never made a fuss again.

Vanessa came in, helped herself to cereal, and sat down on the chair with no seat.

I made a mental note to say nothing about the calves in the barn.

"And after all," I thought to myself, "it is hard to find really secure ground from which to criticize."

Miriam Brown's foundation garments had long since lost their power to restrain. Her hair was stringy, and her clothes, though clean, were a disheartening combination of floral print and polka dot. But I thought perforce of the men I am accustomed to see playing golf at country clubs or gardening in streets that are zoned R-1. I thought of the portly, degenerated figures—the upper arms from which the flesh drips like unsuccessful cake icing, the Bermuda shorts snug around the benevolent parenthesis of the abdomen, but flapping dismally about the skinny knees.

"It must be conceded," I thought, "that merely by being decently covered up, the farmer's wife looks like Aphrodite of Melos compared to what is known as management.

"At any rate," I completed the thought, "management in the summertime."

Harry and I had a pleasantly idle morning, and at half past ten we were sitting on the lawn, our backs to the broken steps and the peeling paint, when a car drove up. It contained (we learned later from Rayleine) Miss Draussman—who is middle-aged and has a clerical job in the big city eighty miles away—and her mother. If Harry and I had not been sitting on the lawn, with our non-Tennessee Williams faces and our reassuring clothes, I am morally certain that Mrs. and Miss Draussman would quickly have put as much distance as possible between themselves and the Brown family's Petit Trianon.

"Where's Rayleine?" I said to Harry, as I saw the visitors freeze. "After all, this is the cash crop."

But Rayleine did not appear, so Harry and I got up and began doing the honors. Mrs. and Miss Draussman had the turn of speech and—it was my intuition—the naked absorption with their own welfare of the lower-middles or lower-lowers or whatever the scientific term is for a shortage of Norman blood. But we gave them no time to think of their own welfare, and just as Harry was lifting the luggage from the car, Rayleine appeared with Cora riding like a dinghy in her wake.

When the Draussmans had been installed in the room down the hall from ours, Rayleine and Cora decided to go swimming, and to Rayleine's considerable annoyance Harry and I said we would go to watch. Rayleine said—and I am sure it was true—that she had been supervising the swimming of younger children for a hundred million years, but I was inflexible. It is my fixed conviction that children can drown in a sizable gin-and-tonic, if I am not there to prevent it; and with all due respect to Rayleine's character-producing environment, I intended in this one particular to be decadent and overprotective.

Harry and I sat down on the hillside and watched Cora and Rayleine wade into the squelchy margin of the little pond, throw themselves into the water, and come up with long brown weeds and drowned grasses sticking to their shoulders and bathing caps.

"That isn't swimming," I said to Harry. "It's liquid botany."

But the children had no fault to find, and we stayed an hour. When we got back, another guest had arrived, and he was so unbelievably strange and anomalous a figure that deportment was taxed to the uttermost to hide the gulp and the stare.

The newcomer's name was Mr. Lemuel Drum. He was a man of about the middle height, but so fantastically slight, delicate and papery of bone structure—so incredibly transparent and ethereal of flesh—that the eye instinctively refused, at first glance, to accept him as human. By way of rounding off the joke that kindly old Mother Nature had played on Lemuel Drum, the wax-pale body was crowned by an outsized and perfectly egg-shaped head. Around the largest part of this ovoid were the remains of some soft, light-brown hair, and well down on the front was an assortment of delicately pinched features.

But paradoxically enough, Mr. Drum—though squeaky of voice and exaggeratedly prissy of manner—was imperturbably self-confident. As we waited in the parlor for lunch, he told us and the Draussmans that he was executive secretary to the president of a moderate-sized corporation. (What a bonanza for the jealous wife, if there should be one!) He said that he had come to Wake-Robin Farm on his vacation for the past several years in a row.

"Not," he said, lowering his voice confidentially, "that I couldn't afford something more modern and streamlined, but I'm writing a book."

He allowed a minute for this to soak in and then added that the Browns' farm was a wonderfully quiet and away-from-it-all place in which to work.

"What kind of book?" I asked.

I expected him to say that it was about the interesting people he met in his work or the crazy things that happened in his office, but he replied calmly, "It's about my dreams. My beautiful dreams."

For Harry and me, this reply taped the newcomer as an improbable blend of William Saroyan and the W.C.T.U. To the Draussmans, on the other hand, it gave an instant feeling of recognition and kinship. They smiled and looked pleased.

"It may not be published in my lifetime," Lemuel Drum said. "I don't know that it will. But I treasure my dreams."

The Draussman ladies nodded.

At this point, Miriam Brown called us in to lunch, which was macaroni and cheese. At lunch, Lemuel Drum performed a service for me, quite unawares, that I had not thought anyone could render. As I watched him chew neatly away at his tiny portion—meanwhile waving the flies off with a tapering, medieval hand—I almost began to feel that flies do not, after all, carry germs. It seemed impossible that pathogenic bacteria could stay alive within a hundred yards of that utterly purified personality.

I could see that our new co-pastoralist had interested and distracted Mrs. and Miss Draussman, too. They looked outraged once or twice as they flapped at the insect life, but for the most part they concentrated on a brisk exchange of personal data with Mr. Drum.

Right after lunch, Lemuel Drum excused himself, and when Harry and I went up to take a nap a little later, we could hear a typewriter clicking away on the floor above.

"The horns of Elfland faintly blowing," Harry said, in a tone wherein compassion mingled with a very perceptible touch of awe.

I had been in a tiny way shocked and disappointed when Mrs. Brown told me the Mellers did not get along. I had not thought of Miriam Brown as the kind of person who would volunteer that sort of information to strangers. But when Mr. and Mrs. Meller arrived immediately after Harry and I came downstairs from our nap, I realized that the Mellers would have felt let down if Mrs. Brown had refrained from telling me.

With some people, being unhappily married is a profession, a vocation as devout as any doctor's or teacher's. One cannot imagine them doing or being anything else. Fortunately, the Mellers are childless, so they are free to concentrate without distraction on the job of being at loggerheads. They arrived flushed and clearly laboring under repressed emotions. Looking angry and all but giving off sparks, Mr. Meller took the suitcases—of which there were a great many—up to the bedroom and did not reappear.

Mrs. Meller was welcomed by the farmer's wife into the family wing of the house. Of softer stuff than her husband, Mrs. Meller was apparently more grieved and hurt than angry. Sartorially, Mrs. Brown and Mrs. Meller provided a striking contrast, for the visitor's dress and accessories were relentlessly matched in every particular and looked as if they had come from the second-act finale of a musical comedy.

"There's such a pathos about it," I said to Harry, "coming to a place like this in an outfit like that.

"And," I predicted, "she'll have a different get-up for every day she's here, and maybe twice on some days."

When the Mellers had disappeared, Harry and I drove to town. Cora stayed behind. She was by this time clearly sorry she had ever met us, and visibly regretted having wasted nine precious years of her life among the urban bourgeoisie.

Harry and I did not go to the little hamlet ten miles away, but to a much larger place in the opposite direction. Our announced purpose was to look for a paperbound book about wild flowers, but I also intended to lay in a supply of cookies. The drive through the pastures and cornfields was beautiful, though I found I was completely cured of looking at farmhouses with the eye of sentimentality.

Getting back to the farm just as people were going in to dinner, we were momentarily staggered at how the guest business had boomed in our absence. There were nineteen people sitting at the dining-room table, and only one was a Brown. (At the head of the table Clarence Brown, in clean blue jeans and neatly pressed plaid cotton shirt, was making a very favorable impression as a sort of Earth Father.)

When I saw this huge ellipse of faces, only one thought interfered with my native American herd instinct . . .

Only one idea marred my bubbling impulse toward camaraderie. . . .

Only one reservation flawed my generous wish to share the delights of Wake-Robin Farm with all and sundry.

That particular thought, however, was a sobering one —namely, that to the best of Harry's and my knowledge, there was only one bathroom.

At the mental picture conjured up by this recollection, I found myself thinking, "Well, I suppose bottle *neck* isn't quite the right word."

But it was scarcely the place to introduce the matter, and there was still room to hope that perhaps the Browns were going to set up portable comfort stations on the front lawn.

Not much could be learned of the new people at dinner, because of the necessity to wave away flies, pass the butter, send the bread on its rounds, respond to requests for the vegetable dishes and see that the big platters of pot roast went from hand to hand. (The Browns' dinner table may have its shortcomings, but there is no denying that it is a wonderful training ground for switchboard operators.)

The first of the new guests I noticed were a family of

man, pregnant wife and three small children, the last seeming to consist mostly of three pairs of very round eyes floating just above the edge of the table. I noticed this family because when we came in, Cora was sitting with the children, cutting up their food, encouraging them to eat—they just wanted to stare—and pushing their milk back from the edge of the table. In one day, Cora was already imitating not only Rayleine's habit of taking on responsibility, but also Rayleine's knack for collecting and transmitting information.

It was from Cora we learned, after dinner, that the father of the three small children is a policeman. From the same source we also learned that the father of another family which appeared at the table—with three older children, more around Cora's age—is an Army sergeant. No Cora was needed to tell us that the sergeant and his wife are Southerners. But despite the Jello-melting-in-the-sun speech pattern, the sergeant's children leap to obey their parents; they call all adults "Sir" or "Ma'am"; and they breathe "crack regiment" from every pore.

The last two newcomers were a Mr. and Mrs. Tullio Riccobono; and Tullio Riccobono, on first encounter, transports one back instantly to the long-forgotten high-school course in Ancient History. Tall, fiftyish, handsome in an aquiline way, with a cap of curls that was once blond and is now nearly all grey, Tullio is everybody's idea of a Roman centurion. You can see him, helmet under arm, strolling with casual arrogance through a conquered town in Gaul. This and no other (you think) is the face that cried "Follow the eagles!" and braced the wavering IXth.

Alas for history! There were a few minutes of conversation in the parlor after dinner, and Harry learned that Tullio Riccobono works in a gas station—and, though apparently the gentlest and most obliging of souls, is probably not relied on very heavily by his boss for administrative decisions and executive aplomb. The Riccobonos have just finished putting their two daughters through college, and they are still so giddy from the cessation of prolonged financial strain that their talk consists of just one sentiment repeated over and over: "At least, we give them something nobody could take away, their education."

The Draussmans, Lemuel Drum and the Mellers were at the dinner table, too, of course—Mrs. Meller ruffled like a petunia in some sort of playsuit thing. One had the feeling that the Mellers saw in the Draussman-Drum constellation a brand-new audience—alert, and not preoccupied with children—for the chronicle of injuries suffered and indignities endured. One had the feeling that husband and wife were already in tense if silent competition to capture those virgin eardrums.

After dinner it occurred to me—correctly, as it turned out—that an extra pair of hands with the dishes might be welcome. When I went out to the high-ceilinged pantry, Mrs. Meller was helping Vanessa and Miriam Brown, while Mr. Meller was visible through the window talking fishing with Clarence Brown.

Wake-Robin Farm has two large deep freezes in the cellar—one of them for venison—and two giant refrigerators rearing up like polar bears in a closet off the kitchen. It has, however, no dishwasher. The guest season runs from May to December, for there is a state forest nearby, and hunters come in the fall. When I looked at the state of the kitchen after eighteen boarders had been fed, it suddenly seemed as if the new phrase which has come into the language—"crash program"—is really rather glib. I doubt if

Miriam Brown has ever in her life seen a program which was *not* "crash."

Later: ~~ That was yesterday.

This morning we learned at breakfast that the pregnant cow had somehow managed to get over or under a barbed wire fence and go A.W.O.L. Presumably, she wanted to "have"—I cannot get my constrained, suburban tongue around that "drop"—her calf in a place of her own choosing. At any rate, when she was discovered to be missing, Henderson Brown mounted the sway-backed white horse and rode around looking for her, but did not find her. So after breakfast all the able-bodied guests, having nothing more urgent to do, formed a sort of posse and went out to search.

The farm covers six hundred acres and the cow apparently had the mettle and pluck which is usually associated with Tom Swift and the Rover Boys. It was noon before we found her, but in the meantime we had spent a delightful morning. We walked far enough apart so as not to be constrained to labor at conversations, and the solid beauty of this farming country—the square fields, cones of silos, cubes of barns and slow arcs of treetops—seemed closer and more immediate because we had a useful reason for being abroad in it.

In the course of the search, we had to cross the field where the Wake-Robin bull was pastured. Though the other guests arrived only yesterday, we have already developed scuttlebutt; and according to the scuttlebutt, even when a bull calf is made a pet of and brought up as one of the family, the bull it grows into is still utterly treacherous. The Wake-Robin bull, so far from being a family pet, had apparently been handled from birth by the dentist who choked Rayleine.

He did not bellow, as our little party crowded gingerly along the farthest edges of his demesne, but he made a loud rumbling noise among his many viscera and tossed his head in what could only be viewed as a sort of practice gore. However, we were a goodly distance away from him, and he seemed to decide that however desirable a spot of bloodletting might be, it was too much trouble to cover the intervening ground.

In the event, it was I who found the cow and her calf. We had looked in all the obvious places. We had searched the stand of pines that Harry and I can see from our window and had combed several bits of woodland that punctuate the arable. I was in the lead as we climbed a hill with some second-growth timber just below its crest, and I thought that through the pencil-marks of saplings I got an impression of hulk and bulk. In a minute I could see the cow and calf, and pausing only long enough to call back that the quarry was located, I ran toward them.

The calf was enchanting in its gawky newness and I felt that the cow and I were fellow-mothers (if there can be such a thing) and was preparing to speak words of felicitation. But the cow put its head down and charged me. I had a split second in which to note that it was like being attacked by a football stadium, and then I screamed for Harry and ran. But the cow only wanted to warn me away from the calf and stopped as soon as I retreated.

Though we had been out all morning, the cow was not actually too far afield, and Henderson soon arrived to cope with defiant motherhood. When we got back to the house, everyone but me collapsed into the rusty garden chairs on the lawn. I went to the barn to round up the children for lunch. I found them—all of them, including Rayleine—sitting in a semi-circle in the loft. Each child—even the policeman's little ones—had hollowed out a cave in the hay, at the mouth of which he sat; and each child was holding in his lap a half-grown chicken.

I do not know what my blood type is, but I am afraid any surgeon who needs a refill for me will have to get it at Schrafft's or some such genteel place, for my first thought was of lice and the fact that chickens are not housebroken. Only secondarily did I marvel that poultry so far from the fluffy, cuddly stage should sit so quietly—beady-eyed, blinking, moving their heads in abrupt little jerks, but apparently entirely content. A half-grown chicken is usually the least impressive of all farmyard animals, but these in their quiescence had a certain unlooked-for dignity. What was most striking, however, was the children's silent wonder and delight at being able to cradle living, feathery things in their arms.

After lunch, when Harry and I were leaning on the unpainted fence, contemplating the pigs, I remarked that it was going to be hard to tear Cora away from this place. Although he is on vacation, Harry has a meeting at the office he must go to when we get back; and while I am getting used to Wake-Robin Farm, I feel no all-conquering impulse to prolong our stay beyond the week we planned.

Fortunately for Cora's peace of mind, one of Harry's relatives is getting married next week with the optimum of pageantry, and Cora has since she was a small child been fascinated with brides. She has a scrapbook filled with clumsily cut-out pictures of them and a collection of dolls dressed in bridal costume, and she has been looking forward to these nuptials as to dawn in Lyonesse. I can imagine what leaving Wake-Robin Farm is going to seem to her—a veritable expulsion from Eden—but let us hope the shock will be cushioned by Mendelssohn and a court train.

July 12th ❧ Harry and I sat up late talking last night. When we were in town the day before yesterday, we bought a bottle of wine and last night seemed as good a time as any to open it. The house was quiet—everyone having gone to bed early—and Cora was fast asleep in the deep shadow left by the one small lamp in our large bedroom. Over the spiritus frumenti, we discussed going to Europe, Harry's job, the characters of our friends, our own characters and the guests at Wake-Robin Farm.

These guests, almost upon the moment of arrival, automatically fell apart into two groups—those with young children and those without. The sergeant's family, the policeman's family and the Fitzgibbonses have a sort of craft guild that rounds up children before meals and gets their hands washed, and at the end of the day bathes off the barnyard mire in a rather small amount of hot water. Between the sergeant, the policeman and Harry there is a manly camaraderie based on cars and mileage and How-do-you-like-the-Giants? (or whatever their name is). The policeman's wife is a fragile, pretty, pathetic thing, seemingly dazed by the succession of pregnancies. The sergeant's wife is just a great big Southern accent that happens to have a woman attached.

In the other (or non-child) camp, things are quite different. Mrs. and Miss Draussman and Mr. Drum are natural-born and instinctive gossips, and they hover over the Mellers' marriage like yellowjackets who have discovered a jam sandwich. This hovering, however, has the full cooperation of the Mellers, in their quite separate and distinct ways. The Draussmans, the Mellers and Lemuel Drum together regard the nearly mute Riccobonos as socially inferior, and endeavor to conceal this belief—well, *almost* to conceal it—by elaborately drawing them into things.

Hapless Riccobonos! I wish I could feel that those daughters they put through college were not already spurning them as insufficiently haut monde; but my intuition about the Riccobonos is that they were born to make great sacrifices and have them go unappreciated. It is not enough in this cruel world to make great sacrifices—you must also be able to dramatize what you have done.

Upon Harry's sympathies, it is not the Riccobonos but Mr. Drum who has made the greatest inroad.

"He doesn't come here to write the book," Harry said. "He writes the book because he has to come here. On his income, he could afford a regular summer resort, but he'd be too conspicuous."

On the general score of camaraderie, I am miles behind Harry. With the Neighborladies at home who burbled when Great-aunt Persis was written up in *Time* and were unmoved when she was savaged by the Legion, there is at least the advantage that we all live in the same place. Conversation, though not Emersonian, comes easily—the Samuel T. Atkinson Grade School, the increasing inefficiency of the trash and garbage pick-up, the traffic congestion downtown, and so on.

Here, it comes less easily. Here I feel as if the novels of Jane Austen that I have loved for so long were soldered around my ankle like a ball and chain—and when I leave our room and go down to dinner, the boarders gathered in the dining room can hear my education clanking on the stair.

Every once in a while, though, there is a tiny break-through, a momentary sense of shared experience. This evening on the porch, the sergeant's two older children (boy and girl) started a fierce and passionate quarrel, and before their autocratic parents could intervene I said, "Why don't you two go and look at television? It's that square box in the living room with the piece of glass in front."

The Browns constitute a neutral background for their guests. An occasional painter stays here—sometimes a grade-school teacher or a botanist—so the farm family is not daunted by the higher learning. They are cheerful, obliging and indifferent with one and all.

"The Browns practice total democracy," I said to Harry last night, as he tilted wine into my glass. "They would no more think of distinguishing between a Fitzgibbons and a Riccobono than they would of distinguishing between one stalk and another of the corn in their fields."

Something in my tone, apparently, made Harry lower his head and look at me professorially from under his brows.

"Don't you approve of total democracy?" he said.

"Not when it includes me."

His guffaw was so loud that I was afraid he would wake Cora.

"*In vino veritas,*" he said.

Later: ❧ I interrupted this to go for a walk with Harry, for the weather has been so wonderful—brilliant and not too hot—that it pulls you as by a form of suction out of the house and down the clean, graveled roads.

To resume . . .

The guests here at Wake-Robin Farm are all urban or semi-urban types; and there are no scenic wonders nearby, no amusement parks, no movies and no stores in which to shop. There is nothing to do but eat, sleep, take walks and look at the farm animals, but nobody seems to be calling for madder music, stronger wine. (Unless possibly it is Mr. Meller, absent now on his fishing trip, who according to the scuttlebutt sits up late looking at television and drinking beer, and stumbles up the stairs.)

Our esprit is of the most superficial and ships-that-pass-in-the-night variety; but esprit it is. Considerateness—a little shrill, but genuine—is shown about helping Miriam Brown in the kitchen, and there are shy courtesies about the bathroom.

The bathroom situation turned out to be not quite so bad as I had imagined, but not very good, either. There is another bathroom in the Browns' wing of the house, and a favored few—Lemuel Drum and the Mellers—are invited to use it. So are the pregnant wife and her small children. But the bathroom down the hall from us . . .

Well, there are times, after everyone has gone to bed, when one imagines that bathroom just lying there in the dark and panting from exhaustion.

In the mornings it is often necessary to wait an exceedingly long time for access to the coveted bit of plumbing. Then, too, the Draussmans use some kind of toilet water or dusting powder that smells exactly like the overly sweet air purifier employed in second-rate movie theaters. And there is also the olfactory circumstance so bluntly referred to by Smollett at the opening of *Humphry Clinker*, a circumstance not helped by the absence of any window. Add to this the dankness of a couple of recent showers and the layered smoke of two or three cigarettes, and anyone with a grain of sensitivity is likely to start entertaining serious doubts about Brotherhood Week.

But it is necessary to take the long view. Harry looked at me sympathetically this morning—he himself had gotten up early—as somebody having the winged foot of Mercury defeated my expectant stance with towel, washcloth, shower cap, soap, toothbrush and toothpaste.

"I refuse to be daunted," I said, replying to his glance. "After all, this is the way of life that turned back the Germans at Stalingrad."

July 13th 🙼 Harry asked me this morning if I still felt the same about the Mrs. Chancellor situation, but as I swiveled around and started to speak, he held up both hands in pretended fright to ward off my eloquence.

"Never mind!" he exclaimed. "I can see it in your face," and said a minute later, "Semper fidelis."

We have two more full days here before we leave; and while it will be heaven to have my own bathroom again, and I shall relish eating my own cuisine—Miriam Brown being what I call a sledgehammer cook—I would not have missed this experience for anything. Never again will I look at my living-room furniture and call it shabby. When I see the sofas and chairs in the Browns' parlor, I do not simply want to throw them on the junk pile. I want to load them into an ambulance and take them to a hospital, for their appearance suggests they are *suffering,* in some kind of dumb, animal way.

This sojourn in the deep country has been an eye-opener; and even in the brief time I have been here, I have had one long-standing question answered for me.

When I used to ride in cushioned ease and blissful ignorance through agricultural areas, I always wondered why so few farmhouses have flower beds around them.

"They must have good soil," I used to think, "and lots of extra manure. Why don't they just sow a few asters and cosmos, instead of letting the grass grow right up to the house?"

But now I know.

When the woman on a family farm has finished a long day of working in double harness and sweet communion with Mother Earth, the last thing in the world she wants to see is a home-grown zinnia. When the woman on a family farm has finished her day's work, what she wants to look at is something incapable of supporting vegetation—like, for instance, a flight of subway stairs.

July 15th ✎ This morning those of us who have children went with our offspring to watch Fanshawe and Henderson harvest a field of peas. I had visualized the peas as being picked—pod by pod—but actually the method is to claw the whole plant up from the ground and toss it on a truck. Thence it is taken to the canning factory seventeen miles away.

In the afternoon, we all went to the factory to watch the Wake-Robin peas being canned. Upon notice, the factory is glad to show visitors around, and it has quite a few, for a number of the farms hereabouts supplement their incomes by taking in vacationers.

Not large as present-day establishments go, the factory proved to be idyllically located in the midst of orchards, with dancing light and shade on the loading platforms and horses grazing just beyond a nearby fence. However, when Harry and I, looking for the office, walked round to the back, we found something I had never seen before and whose existence I had never imagined—namely, a mound of decayed vegetation more than twenty feet high and about fifty feet in circumference. It gave off such a choking, suffocating, overpowering stench that we clapped handkerchiefs to our noses and tried not to breathe; but we saw workmen walking unconcernedly back and forth right next to it with no signs of distress.

Inside, the smell did not pursue us beyond a certain distance. Inside, there were bubbling vats, jigging pistons, humming fan belts and spiraled pipes. There were things that hissed, things that slammed and banged, and things that squealed. A secretary person showed us around—yelling demurely in the noisier places—and we learned that the factory often cans fruit and vegetables for companies whose brand names are household words. We were shown huge stacks of the labels I am accustomed to see on Monday morning, when trucks the size of three-bedroom houses warp themselves with heartbroken sigh of airbrake to the back and sides of Plethora, Inc., and men in visored caps and semi-uniforms, with brand names embroidered in silk over their hearts, decant comestibles for the overweight consumer.

On our guided tour, the secretary person consistently referred to the management of the canning factory as "They." And while—as Harry said—"They" could scarcely be expected to employ a Henry Thoreau or a Thorstein Veblen to show people around, the secretary's nunlike reverence and gentle acclaim for "Their" policies sounded more like the cathedral close than the market place.

This reverence the guests of Wake-Robin Farm, childless and parents alike, met more than halfway. As they asked their respectful questions, you could see the stereotype clutching their minds like the eagle's talons grasping the arrows over the ribbon that says, "E Pluribus Unum." This was Business—reliable, energetic, unfailing, clean, cheerful, practical, friendly, well disposed and world-conquering.

It remained for Mrs. Brown, at the dinner table this evening, to bring the applause for free enterprise to an abrupt halt. When old Mrs. Draussman, parroting the secretary, explained to the world in general how good the canning factory is to its personnel, Miriam Brown looked sourly amused.

"They're not good to the farmer," she said. "They don't pay till November."

July 22nd ❧ We have been home for five days, and it was delicious to slip back into our old life and habits. However, the week at Wake-Robin Farm has left its echoes behind. Good echoes. Now when I contemplate the advertisements in the Sunday papers—page after page after page of magic casements opening on the foam of the Not-Yet-Bought—I think of the Ford Foundation outside of the farm's kitchen door and I feel a little less swamped and more stabilized.

Also, the first evening back, we spent an hour telling Russ and Cynthia all about it, and Cora very amiably and—apparently—competently stayed with the little boys.

This is something she has always previously had to be dragooned into doing, and the new attitude can only be explained as the influence of Rayleine.

July 25th 〰 The daytime nightmare of Mrs. Chancellor, Great-aunt Persis and the Women's Liberal Club has uncoiled yet another little vista of unloveliness. Harry is still on vacation; and he and I were sitting under the trees this noon when Cynthia, in high heels and good clothes, came running with light, quick, angry tread up the uneven stone steps from the street.

The time is approaching when Cynthia will have to write to India and break the news that the favor Great-aunt Persis did for the Women's Liberal Club has been tossed unwanted back into her lap. Mrs. Chancellor seems not to have written; and indeed there has been a kind of hideous slow motion about the whole affair, ever since the Legion intervened—as if all the people involved were skin-diving in jellied consommé.

Friend Cynthia has sometimes reminded me of white iris—the blossom so ethereal and poised for flight, but the stem strong and the leaves shaped like broadswords. I thought of the comparison again when she dropped into the chair Harry offered and announced that she had just come from seeing Dr. Aspirin and asking him whether St. Euphoria would, as a liberal church, take over the invitation Mrs. Chancellor and her Executive Committee had withdrawn. Cynthia had not said anything to anyone about going, because even we who love her had indicated that she was riding the subject too hard.

Cynthia does not attend St. Euphoria—or, for that matter, any church—and she knows that Harry and I do not consider Dr. Aspirin another Fra Angelico (except in looks). But I should not have called her a white iris. She is a Bulldog Drummond, disdaining defeat when everybody else has sensibly conceded it.

She is also unconniving and innocent enough—possibly because so much of her mind is taken up with painter-thoughts—to have mentioned Harry and me when calling for an appointment. (It did not occur to her that if the Fitzgibbonses are not enthusiastic about Dr. Aspirin, Dr. Aspirin probably reciprocates.)

Owing to this guilelessness, Dr. Aspirin was aware that, whatever was being lobbed in his direction, it was more likely to be a cactus than a Fortnum & Mason brandied peach.

The parson fielded it neatly.

He began with the conventional expressions of horror that so admirable a person as Great-aunt Persis should receive such treatment, and he even used the word "caitiff." (Cynthia asked us what it meant.) I had thought no one but me was still getting mileage out of this beautiful Elizabethan term of opprobrium, and I was reminded once again of how much I would admire Dr. Aspirin if only he had a little fighting spirit.

However, having made the usual deploring noises, the curé explained that St. Euphoria is having a membership drive in the fall. If the church were to sponsor a lecturer who was picketed by the American Legion, if the local paper were full of letters from the Thrumborough Radical Right describing Great-aunt Persis as a friend of the Chinese Communists, it would scare away (Dr. Aspirin said) many troubled people who need the help of liberal religion.

If only, the pastor lamented, this opportunity to do honor to a woman like Great-aunt Persis had come at some other time!

"But," said Cynthia, "I should think that if you were picketed by the American Legion, you'd get just the type of new members you want."

Harry's eyes sparkled, and I made a convulsive movement toward the house, my impulse being to telephone some of St. Euphoria's long-time members and tell them that old Love-Thy-Enemy had just taken one right on the chin.

I stopped myself, however, for, according to Cynthia's account, Dr. Aspirin was not dismayed. He parried deftly.

"We don't want to talk to the already persuaded," he said. "Or at least, not only to them. We also want to reach the confused, unhappy sort of person who hasn't thought things through yet."

Then—in the kindliest and most understanding way— he earnestly advised Friend Cynthia to let the whole matter drop. Jim Afterbirth himself, the parson averred, is not a bad egg, but Maida Chancellor was right in saying that there are some really evil reactionaries over in Thrumborough.

"They're compulsive, they're obsessive, they're hysterical," he said, and went on to observe that the people who should be on the side of the angels were sick to death of the Communist issue and would not rally round.

"How do you know till you try?" Cynthia asked.

But Dr. Aspirin blandly overrode her. He had not, he said, been a minister in this locality for ten years without learning to read the public pulse.

"The meeting would be picketed," he warned. "Make no mistake about that. Afterbirth would hate to do it, but the Legion has a State Committee on Un-Americanism and they ride herd. It would be thoroughly unpleasant."

As Cynthia recounted her answer—that St. Euphoria had been picketed before, and by the American Legion— I found that I was suddenly and most distractingly a prey to waves of fright. My heart had begun to pound, and I could not get a proper lungful of air. Some recollection, painful and piercing, but as yet unidentified, seemed to be trying to make its way into my mind.

I heard Cynthia's voice going on. The minister appeared to have said in a dozen different ways that he felt all the force of Cynthia's arguments; but there was always some cogent reason why he had to decline the honor of Great-aunt Persis's appearance.

The elusive memory that had diverted me from Cynthia's story appeared to have something to do with the weather—with the gorgeous, panoplied July day, all phlox and butterflies, sweeping its golden embroideries over the little gardens and the rather close-set houses stepping down the hill.

Cynthia's account continued; and Dr. Aspirin evidently lost, as the discussion proceeded, some of the kindliness and understanding with which he had started out. He wanted to know what the Legion "had" on Great-aunt Persis, and seemed annoyed, Cynthia said, that she and I had refused to look at Mrs. Chancellor's purple-printed list of accusations.

It is amazing how you can be in the middle of a conversational group and suffer the *crise des nerfs* of a lifetime without anyone's noticing. Cynthia talked. Harry asked questions. I sat silently battling an all-submerging, nameless fear—and nothing about me, apparently, showed what I was feeling. I could not pin my emotion down. It was certainly not that I was surprised by the minister's sidestepping, since I had known for a long time that a woman scrubbing down her kitchen shelves can show cards and spades to Dr. Aspirin when it comes to moral fervor.

So all day long the noise of battle rolled. Cynthia told Dr. Aspirin that a lot of people are getting tired of the Legion's tactics; and Dr. Aspirin said he has men in his congregation who work for the government and who have to think of their security clearance.

My interior panic seemed to be subsiding, but I was still raked by a memory that felt supremely urgent and yet would not take definite form.

Returning to his kindly manner, Dr. Aspirin said that Cynthia, with an innocence that in any other situation he would applaud and cheer on, was thinking of a good clean fight. However (the dominie said) it would not be a good clean fight: the McCarthyites in Thrumborough are lunatics.

Cynthia, displaying the first streak of humor I have ever known in her beautiful but earnest character, retorted, "So was George the Third."

Nevertheless, bon mot to the contrary and notwithstanding, she had failed to accomplish her mission; and what depressed me most from her account was how easily Dr. Aspirin had been able to persuade himself that he was doing the moral thing in letting Great-aunt Persis's detractors go unreproached.

"To the vicar belong the spoils" was the sentence that went moodily through my mind, and suddenly I knew what it was that had frightened me and what I had been trying to think of.

The canning factory.

The canning factory—the beautiful day—the idyllic setting—and there in the midst of all the tranquility and abundance, the mound of spoiled and rotting matter and the workmen strolling through the stench, so conditioned to it that it had come to seem like normal air. I had a fleeting twinge of amusement at how little either Mrs. Chancellor or Dr. Aspirin would relish being compared to over-alled, lunchbox-toting factory hands. My next thought, however, was probably the nearest thing to a prayer that has been distilled out of my psyche since I left the Protestant Episcopals many years ago.

"Let us not get used to it, Cynthia and I. No matter how many people adjust to the Great-aunt Persises being expendable, let Cynthia and me not get used to it."

I realized what had panicked me—the sudden pre-conscious intimation that if enough time passed, and if we did not fight it off determinedly enough, even Cynthia and I might eventually end up being just like Dr. Aspirin. Or that five-star Brownie, Mrs. Chancellor. I had a stabbing pang of self-reproach that I had thought Cynthia too intense about Mrs. Chancellor.

It was just at this moment that Harry said speculatively, "I wonder if it would do any good for you two to go around and see Meinert van Lier."

He added apologetically that of course he was just grasping at straws and I said in some surprise, "I didn't know Meinert van Lier was still alive."

"He's quite old," Harry said, "but he still goes down to the office once in a while."

He turned to Cynthia.

"He used to serve on one of my boards of directors, and I know him well enough to send you around."

At this point we had to explain to Cynthia ("Don't look now," I said to her, "but your birthday is showing") that

Meinert van Lier is a lawyer who was in his heyday a famous champion of freedom of opinion.

"I'm absolutely positive," Harry said, "that I'm sending you on a wild-goose chase."

He hesitated and then went on.

"It's only that a kind of blackmail is operating here . . . and I just wondered whether, if a lawyer wrote to Jim Afterbirth . . . if he asked Afterbirth whether the Thrumborough Post of the Legion would care to withdraw its objections to Great-aunt Persis, or else prove their validity in court . . ."

"To meet threat with threat?" I suggested. "To see whether maybe they aren't just bluffing?"

Cynthia, hot and tired and angry, had brightened so much at the prospect of still being able to do something that Harry had to remind her this was in all likelihood just another will-o'-the-wisp.

She sighed and her radiance dimmed.

"Do we need the list when we go to Meinert van Lier?" I asked Harry. "The one Mrs. Chancellor had from the records of the Whatsis Committee?"

"The Senate Internal Security Sub-Committee," Harry replied. "Better known to us subversives as the Senate Eternal Impurity Sub-Committee.

"Yes," he added, "you'd better have it. Just call up Mrs. Chancellor and say you've changed your minds and you'd like to see it."

Cynthia stood up and prepared to go, and, looking at her, I realized that whatever might happen in the future, at the present she was certainly not resigned to the behavior of the Women's Liberal Club.

Harry walked Cynthia home, and I sat on under the trees, thinking about Great-aunt Persis and the canning factory and feeling like the heart bowed down, if ever there was one. When Harry came back, I said, "You call the sitter while I take a shower. We're going in to the city."

Though he looked a question, he seemed as if he already suspected the answer.

"We'll see a play or go to a museum and look at some pictures," I said. "I just have to get away."

Harry put his arm around me in a rather rough embrace.

"The natives are restless tonight," he said.

July 27th ❧ I keep my recipes in a card index box, and Cora came running into the dining room this morning, where I was sorting laundry, exclaiming, "Mommy! I opened your recipes and a spider ran out of the D's!"

Yesterday she found two bluejay feathers on the lawn and we thumbtacked them to the window frame above the kitchen sink, where they look very striking (and undomestic) with their haughty iridescence and their dramatic black crossbars. Most people around here dislike the jays because of their noise, and I hate their noise, too; but to me blue in nature—delphinium, bluejays, the summer sea or the eyes of Siamese cats—is the most magnificent and surprising thing there is.

A nature note of a somewhat less exalted kind was provided for me this morning by finding ants on the kitchen floor. Upon investigation, it developed that Cora and Harry, standing in front of the refrigerator last week eating cherries, had not bothered to put the pits in the garbage pail. They simply spat them into the narrow aperture between the refrigerator and the wall.

I brought the matter up at the dinner table this evening, the general tenor of my communication being along the lines of Zola's *J'Accuse!*

"Why," I said, horror blending with incredulity, "it was a filthy thing to do. How *could* you?"

"We just went puh-*too*," said Cora.

Friend Cynthia called Mrs. Chancellor yesterday. Mrs. C. has by now become so guilt-ridden at the mere mention of Cynthia's name that, give her a small supply of iambic pentameter, and she could pass for Lady Macbeth in the sleepwalking scene. Cynthia asked to have the Eternal Impurity list on Great-aunt Persis sent to her, was told in a dazed way that her request would be complied with, and had hung up before the usually very brisk and positive Mrs. Chancellor had finished stammering. Mrs. C had no chance to ask what the list was wanted for.

July 30th ‏‏‎ There is an inconsistency about suburban wives and mothers which haunts me all summer long. In the warm weather, my homemaking colleagues almost invariably—regardless of age, shape or status—wear sleeveless blouses and Bermuda shorts; and when you see them walking toward you, you cannot help but notice that the mammary development is constrained, rigid and unmoving. The wired points of the bosom bear down on the observer like gun turrets, and the "separation" is as unmistakable as Bering Strait.

However, when these gentle ironclads, these female *Monitors* and feminine *Merrimacs,* turn around and walk away, the eye is confronted with such a plunging and such a rhythmic jiggling as to suggest the interior of a churn. Is it the sign of a schizophrenic culture, I wonder—the woman so mannered and artificial in the front, so extremely earthy in the back?

As a matter of fact, it is a marvel that no sartorial Tom Paine has yet arisen to point out that the Bermuda short itself is a disfiguring garment.

Disfiguring?

It is utterly heartless.

It cuts off from public view the bland, supportive thigh, leaving only the scowling kneecap to carry, artistically speaking, the torso's weight. It does not flirt and twirl like a kilt. It merely cants, like a couple of old stovepipes thrown down in a vacant lot. To the flying buttock, it is merciless; and an opulent roundness of stomach—which drape of trouser or decorum of skirt can sometimes render not unpleasing—becomes a canteloupe supported on lollipop sticks.

The summer is a strenuous time, in the United States, for the aesthetician, what with the indignity of the Bermuda short and the widely prevalent habit of wearing the shirt tails out. The news magazines talk ad infinitum ad nauseam about our high standard of living; but the ironic fact is that in warm weather, this country looks like the examining room of an understaffed Ukrainian clinic.

The thoughts of the housewife are long, long thoughts; and the lonely hours of cutting down bedspreads into café curtains or cooking up things for the freezer against company coming next week are often filled with fantasies and speculations. Some of these fantasies and speculations would cause the males of the society, could they know about them, considerable alarm in behalf of the status quo.

For instance, I have often wondered, during the summer months, whether we would not have a stronger foreign policy, make more progress toward rights for Negroes and secure a better educational system for the children if we forgot about "comfort"—which we have too much of anyway—and insisted on dressing with beauty and dignity. If we wore the toga of Cincinnatus or the chiton of Socrates—or at least something closer to such garments than Bermuda shorts—might we not begin to resemble those dignitaries in our conduct of public affairs?

(I shall never forget Harry's scorn and outrage when the sack dress came into fashion. "That's what women would have looked like," he said, "if Eve hadn't eaten the apple.")

How much do our clothes unconsciously influence the way we behave?

Take the Madonna of the Suburbs as she sets out to do her errands on an August morning. In reality, she is a decent soul, laboring with commendable persistence (if not always with success) to keep her family away from psychiatry, bankruptcy, conformity and possibly barratry and simony.

But does she *look* like a decent soul?

Does anything about her suggest the warm and comforting materfamilias?

Her hair is fluffed out and puffed out in a style which has a piquant name in the pages of *Vogue,* but which is actually just plain burst-mattress. Her eyes are blanked out by sunglasses, so that the impersonal black hollows of the meatless skull substitute for the warm, revealing, human glance. Her lips, on the other hand, are strongly accented with brightly colored unguents, so that, if the upper part of the face is cadaver, the lower part is carnivore.

She wears, our suburban Ceres, Bermuda shorts; and dangling from fingertips and banging against her bare legs—which may or may not be shapely—is a purse or handbag so huge as to suggest that what she has got inside is a small Congressman. To complete this bare garishness, this undraped and denuded eccentricity, she wears playshoes or slippers. This footgear is entirely and uncompromisingly heelless and gives the impression that the wearer is not walking on top of the sidewalk, but wading through it about an inch and a half below the surface.

Should that mythical invader from Mars ever swoop to the ground in front of this loyal wife and devoted mother, he would not say, "Take me to your leader." He would turn to his fellow Martians and remark, "Name it and you can have it."

August 3rd 〜 The weather is hot, grey and muggy. It is rather like, in fact, an unwelcome caress, having that same quality of seeming intolerably prolonged. (Or am I the only one who remembers having been kissed in childhood by uncles with wet lips? And they were uncles, so you dassent wipe it off.) Everything is damp. Drawers stick. Stamps are pasted to each other like young lovers. Mildew forms on the side of the refrigerator. Tempers flash out.

Meinert van Lier is in the hospital with a slight respiratory ailment. It is not serious, except as any infirmity is serious for a person his age. If he recovers, we can see him in about ten days or two weeks. But the weather, of course, is not helping him any.

August 5th ❧ What I have been thinking this morning is that there are breakers ahead for Cora and me if Cora turns out to get—as they tell me the older children do—innumerable phone calls. I am basically so optimistic that whenever the phone rings, my heart leaps up like old Brother Wordsworth's at the sight of a rainbow. It is my invariable and instinctive conviction that that shrill summons is good news.

Perhaps some eminent portrait painter has seen me on the street and said to himself, "Not for me the conventionally beautiful woman! It is those provocative (if irregular) features I must paint!"

Before I even get to the instrument—while I am still racing up from the cellar or streaking in from the yard—my ego is expanded and glowing and in my mind gracious phrases of acceptance are already formed.

("Paint *me?* Li'l ole me?")

Then I pick up the receiver and a small chirp of a voice that might be coming out from under a toadstool says —with the usual slovenly pronunciation—"Hullo'sCora-there?"

Since there is no possibility that in either this life or the next I will ever be able to hear a phone ring and say calmly to myself, "That's probably for Cora," I can see the inevitable outcome. Cora will end up as that famous character of song and story, the rejected child. I can even imagine there being a popular ditty about it, a hill-billy canticle, perhaps, or a ballad called *Cora Fitzgibbons* that would begin

> "I got nuthin' but a peer group,
> My mammy done left me alone.
> She couldn't stand hearing the Brownies,
> Whenever she answered the phone."

August 8th ✒ Harry has been more than usually deep-buried in books and reading for the last few weeks, and tonight, coming out of the little study off the living room, he handed me next fall's lesson plan for his ninth-grade Sunday-school class. He had a smile of conscious achievement, and I saw that to the usual material about comparative religion which he has been doing for several years —Confucianism, Hinduism, Islam, etc.—he had added some new topics:

Roman Stoicism and Epicureanism	Reference to today
Wars of Religion	Why people fight about belief
Atheism and Agnosticism	The faith of "the unbeliever"
Poetry and Belief	Lyrics by Frost and Millay
Existentialism	Some new religious adventures of today, names, terms, etc.

"Those young people," I said enviously, when I had finished reading, "are going to end up knowing a lot more than I do."

His mockery for once forgotten, Harry looked extremely pleased.

"It's just what a lesson plan should be," I said. "Chewy."

Harry is riding high with his Sunday-school class now, but his teaching started off disastrously. Well, not disastrously perhaps, but dismayingly. The first year the teacher-pupil situation simply did not work. Not that he had a discipline problem—he has too sharp a tongue for that—but attendance was poor. When the children did come—forced, one suspected, by their parents—gulfs and chasms separated the teacher from the taught.

Vocabulary and attitude alike proclaimed that Harry was geared to adults; and this barrier, once visible, is almost impossible to break down. Self-conscious and chagrined, flooded with teaching materials but alien in spirit, Harry struggled on, but he intended to give the whole thing up when the year was completed. However, there was a great shortage of Sunday-school teachers; no one was available to take his place; and Harry Fitzgibbons is practically the archetype of the responsible man. Grim but dutiful, he said he would carry on and then—*mirabile dictu!*—he got a wonderful class, and instead of his teaching the class, the class taught him.

They are scattered and gone now, those young people, most of them in college, but they had a group spirit that got Harry unstuck and their memory is still green in the Fitzgibbons household. Harry has never again had so distinctive and rewarding a ninth grade, but he has never again needed it.

He has a reputation now.

"Mr. Fitzgibbons is funny," the children say. "You have to laugh."

Not all of them like him. Some of them, I think, inarticulately resent the demandingness of the standards he believes in. (Do they get that from home, one wonders?) But he is established, and the girls often get crushes on him. To Harry there has been something peculiarly substantial and gratifying about this eventual success—a reward, in the push-button age, for old-fashioned, dogged, unexpectant virtue.

August 10th ❧ Nobody can talk about anything but the weather. It passes belief—more than a solid week now of wet, oppressive, unsunlit, enervating heat.

Only the air-conditioned can get anything done; newspaper headlines about the discomfort take precedence over the fall of empires; and Harry said that the sod he would like to get hold of is the one who called this the North Temperate Zone.

Every day I look at the obituaries in fear and trembling for Meinert van Lier, but to date the gallant old fellow has held out.

August 12th ❧ The books and publications I read have made me acutely conscious of how many people in the world do not get enough to eat.

But this information, though I would not lightly expunge it from my mind, puts me in an anomalous position.

To wit:

The doctors say that due to automobiles and not living close to the soil, we carry around too much weight and will expire prematurely of heart attacks unless we cut down on rich foods.

Furthermore, although I try till the veins stand out on my forehead not to be influenced by the cult of slimness, honesty (there's the *real* bitch goddess for you!) requires the confession that I actually am influenced by it. Very much so.

But the eyes of Asia are upon me.

So here I stand in the midst of the Low-Cal, the No-Cal, the salt-free, the fat-free, the skim milk, the cottage cheese, the weight-control bread, the appetite-killing pills and the all-protein ice cream.

And I can almost hear those people who live on a handful of rice a day saying, "Why does she have to compound the irony?

"Look," those people say, "at the six- and eight-page throwaways from the chain stores listing their 'specials.' And those are only the bargains! They have mountains of stuff besides that's not on sale.

"If she lives in the midst of such a glut"—I can hear those people saying—"the least she can do is eat. It makes a mockery of our fate, to diet in the midst of plenty."

And so I get the addendum of fat around the waist and feel unlovely.

The Eternal Impurity Sub-Committee should but know how often I have wanted to take a good half of the food in this town and give it to the hungry, and no questions asked about their political beliefs.

August 13th ➤ Jan Struther said in *Mrs. Miniver* that the most gratifying circumstance of marriage is not any of the big, important things, but the fact of there always being an eye to catch. What I think most gratifying about marriage, however, is the conversational shorthand. Though perhaps, come to think of it, they are much the same thing.

We had dinner last night with some of Harry's relatives who live about an hour's drive away. While we were still with our hosts, a torrential downpour temporarily relieved the still-persisting mugginess and heat. On the way home, the air was cool; the tires splashed; we had the happy consciousness of family duty done; and Cora was asleep on the back seat with her eyelashes lending a fabulous, legendary, Helen-of-Troy note to the commonplace interior of our automobile.

Half the journey had been accomplished in silence when Harry said without preamble, " '. . . firm, impassioned *stress?* ' "

"Yup," I said, nodding.

> " 'Oh, beautiful for pilgrim feet,
> Whose firm, impassioned stress,
> A thoroughfare for freedom beat
> Across the wilderness.' "

After a minute, I added, "Freedombeat always seems to me like one word. A medical term, perhaps. The name of a ductless gland."

"Oh, no!" Harry said authoritatively. "Not a gland, a bone. You often see it in the papers: 'Mr. Smith was taken to the hospital with a gangrenous condition of the freedombeat.' "

August 15th ❦ How full of disagreeable surprises life is! I went in to the kitchen this afternoon and found

Young Cat and Old Cat sitting side by side, in identical postures, on the kitchen chair. They were the very quintessence of Siamese lordliness. Four chocolate paws drooped in neat alignment over the front edge of the chair. The dark triangles of their ears slashed sharply through the circumambient air, and the cream-colored fur of their chests had an opulence right out of Titian. As I came in, their blue eyes—tilted slightly back, like expensive plates on display in a store window—surveyed me with remote, impersonal blandness.

Then I glanced through the door and saw that one of them had regurgitated copiously on the dining-room rug, which—having a sort of sculptured or bas-relief design— is the most difficult one in the house for removal of alien substances.

" 'Nature red in tooth and claw,' " I said to my pets in a grating voice as I fetched hot water and the roll of paper towels and tried to keep myself from the full realization of how revolted I was.

"You don't fool me with your posing."

Harry is supposed to take care of messes like that. I am assumed to be a bundle of feminine sensibilities, too finely organized for such rough employment. The only trouble is, the cats *never* throw up when Harry is home.

Nor do children.

"Other men," I once remarked dourly to my husband, "are said to make people's hearts miss a beat. But one look at you settles the stomach."

August 18th ❧ I need not have worried, when my tooth stopped hurting after I lied to the dentist, that the Puritan system of rewards and punishments had become inoperative. It is still operating about the weather. We are being made to pay—with a miserable, sticky, oppressive August—for our resplendent June and July. Today it is so damp and breathless that one perspires at the slightest movement, and the sky is white and opaque—it is, in fact, as if we were under the lid of one of those covered vegetable dishes. I shall think twice, next winter, before I slam the top on the bowl of string beans and imprison the poor little things in their own steam. I know now what it feels like.

Nevertheless, Meinert van Lier is home from the hospital, although it will be a little while before we can see him. Cynthia and I are nervously awaiting word—for time, on the Great-aunt Persis situation, is beginning to run out.

August 23rd ～ When I was baby-sitting with Cynthia's boys the other day, I was compelled to take one of her history-of-art books out of the bookcase to read. "Compelled," odd though it sounds, is the right word; for I am a sort of print alcoholic, and in my idle moments will read letterheads and the complete texts of eczema advertisements rather than read nothing at all.

Cynthia and Russ, on the other hand, though readers, are not compulsive about it. The only book that happened to be on their living-room table the other day was a rental-library copy of a best-seller, and it was one of the genre that could best be described as vocational novels.

In these vocational novels—and there seems to have been a flood of them in the last few years—the hero of the story is really the public-relations business or the advertising business or the investment-trust business or the salami business; while the material with which the classical novelists used to work—namely, human beings—comes off a very bad and cardboardy second.

Of course, the vocational novels are actually intended to deal not with the business itself but with the businessman who runs or helps to run it; but the authors have failed to realize (it seems to me) that that particular project is self-defeating. There will never be an "important" book about the businessman qua businessman because when the stakes are only prosperity, even the businessman himself does not basically give a damn. A great deal of business was done in Thackeray's England—in fact, commerce was the dominant preoccupation of the age—but the author of *Vanity Fair* was not so foolish as to think there was a novel in who was pushing whom off those tall stools in the countinghouse.

Such being my opinion of novels about the businessman, I chose the history of art for entertainment and distraction; and although it was full of words like "metope," of which I did not know the meaning, I came across a sentence about Piero della Francesca saying that he painted trees coming out of the ground in a rather cavalier and arbitrary fashion because he was interested in trees only as objects in space and not as things that grow. It made me think of the way the earth presses up to meet the roots of trees, and the way the roots plunge out and down to meet the earth, so that the whole relationship, though it may seem to the quick glance (or to Piero della Francesca) like a mere slash or straight line, is actually full of muted sinuosities.

How like the imperceptible curves and twists and variants and flowing-melting lines that occur in the warring equilibrium between the generations! (This comparison occurred to me at Cynthia's, I am sure, because I have so often locked antlers with her stubborn younger son.)

One of the worst vicissitudes of rearing children is the panic the parent feels when it appears that—through the instrumentality of his child, over whom he has a quite insufficient control—he, the parent, is going to be disgraced. I get a good healthy inkling of this feeling when I discover that Cora has taken advantage of my being involved in the cellar with the family wash to sneak off to school in a soiled dress and with a great, sluttish snarl clearly visible in her hair. I always have to resist an impulse to call the school office and explain that although Cora may go around ostentatiously using Harry's and my name, we are really just taking care of her to accommodate a friend.

On the other hand, I am more than resigned to being her mother when her childishness manifests itself in less socially fracturing ways. As when, for instance, she has just thrown a double in Parchesi—or learned that there will be no school on Columbus Day—and she sways from side to side in a forty-five-degree arc and exclaims with incredulous joy, "Oi, Kuh-*foy*, Kuh-*fooey!* I'm *fainting!*"

Nor do I feel like disowning her when I sit in Harry's and my bedroom of an evening, taking up hems in the dresses my daughter inherits from the daughter of a man in Harry's office, and hear the sound of voices from Cora's room, where Harry is sitting on the edge of the bed giving ear to Cora's version of *My Day.*

Cora's voice sounds like a very small but quickly flowing brook, and, like a brook, it races on without pause; but every once in a while there is a far-distant train whistle or fog horn, and that is Harry's heavier tone, interposing briefly with question or reply. I cannot usually distinguish the words of this exchange—it is just alternations of sound—but once in a while a fragment will come in clearly.

CORA: There was this boy and Daddy he had the most wonderful—

HARRY: Not "this" . . . "a." There was *a* boy . . .

CORA: *A* boy. There was this boy and Daddy he had the most wonderful . . .

But the earth does not only support and nourish its trees. It also grapples with them, and mention of the sound of voices reminds me that, just as some noises are so high and thin that only dogs can hear them, so, inversely, there are courteous requests that dogs and adults can hear but which are completely inaudible to children.

When all my good-natured—nay, positively fluting!—attempts to communicate with Cora have drawn a blank, I have to fall back on the coarse techniques of the drill sergeant.

"Cora Fitzgibbons! You get down here *this minute* and set the table!"

A languid and unhasting footfall echoes on the stair, and then Cora comes into the kitchen with a countenance I can only describe as looking like a swamp. It has that same unpleasant calm.

"You don't have to get so mean," she says. "You never asked me."

Like the conjunction of tree and earth, there are sometimes greater tensions in a family situation than commonplace observation would suggest. Certainly, a deeper involvement than we realized at the time characterized the

Thirty Years War between Cora and her parents about buying a dishwasher.

We are a small family and we eat a small breakfast, so it seemed to Harry and me that we would not be grinding in the faces of the poor if we required Cora to feed the cats and wash the breakfast dishes in the morning, in return for her weekly allowance. But Cora—according to her own privately conducted poll—was absolutely the only child in the United States that had to immerse its tender digits in primitive, obsolescent dishwater. The families of all the others, bar none, performed the humiliating chore by machine.

Since Harry and I were determined on saving money for a trip to Europe, Cora—on the dishwasher issue—was beaten before she started. But oh, what a long time it took her to find out! She mounted so solid an offensive—she whined, she wept, she coaxed and she returned so persistently to the attack—that if there had been within the remotest Patagonian hinterlands of my mind the tiniest wish for a dishwasher, Cora might have had her way. But whenever Cora thought "dishwasher," I thought "Cunarder," so she could not win.

While it lasted, however, the dishwasher controversy was a time that tried men's souls. For one thing—possibly because Cora is small and slight for her age—it is always my feeling that I should not get right down there in the gutter and slug it out with her as an equal. My dream and my ideal is to have perfect control over my anger, judiciously permitting it to flash out here and there for the sake of dramatic effect, but never helplessly swept away by it.

Ah, me! I learned long ago what a vain, idle, fruitless, bootless fancy *that* is!

In the dishwasher contest, what got me down lip to lip and nose to nose with Cora in a perfect democracy of rage—and how degraded I felt about it afterward!—was her imperviousness to either fairness or reason. To the idea that she ought to help out a little in return for her allowance she would make no concession at all. And although the point was reiterated endlessly, she could not see that it takes her less time to wash, dry and put away our few plates and cups than it takes her friends—in three- and four-child families where they breakfast like Percherons—to load the dishwasher.

Clenched fists were raised to heaven, and the expanding universe was queried as to why our daughter could not get it through her *head* . . . The dishwasher issue, in short, was the Middle East of our family set-up.

Ultimately, time elapsed, feelings subsided, and the matter receded into history; and later on Harry and I agreed, with the penetration of hindsight, that the passion on both sides of the debate came from something more than a mere labor-saving device.

So far as Cora was concerned, if she could get us to buy something we did not wish to buy, on the ground that all her friends had it, she would have acquired what used to be known in the chancelleries of Europe as hegemony. With Harry and me, it was not just Cora speaking. It was the whole society we live in, exercising all its sovereignty to shove us down the Skid Row of home improvement.

But time and the hour runs through the roughest day, and our daughter at long last became resigned to the fate which has landed her, without hope of rescue, in her father's and mother's household. When she was on the phone the other day, I heard her alluding in a tone of settled melancholy to the fact that she has to wash the dishes in the morning.

"The radio is my one comfort," she said.

August 25th ❧ Another one of those books about the suburbs is being passed from hand to hand and mentioned in every conversation; and I said to Harry at breakfast this morning that I am beginning to get fed up with these volumes. They are always written by a class of people I call Measurers, and whether they come from Madison Avenue or from the loftier purlieus of a university, Measurers always find everybody alike because they *want* to find everybody alike. They pretend to be shocked at conformity, but it is only a pretense.

People see what they want to see (I said to Harry at breakfast this morning). When I drive through the development or up the steep streets of our hill, my impression is less that I am surrounded by conformists than that the people who live here have secrets and they have problems.

There is an old couple in a house at the end of our street whose only son lives in Spain and—they hear by roundabout means—does well financially. But he has not written to his parents in years, and they are just hanging on to life in the hope that they will hear from him before they die. Is he paying them back for some earlier injury done to him, or are they suffering undeservedly? Who can say? But the answer is not one that can be discovered by checking off printed cards like the one the lady pollster handed me last winter.

❧*195*

On the street back of us a pretty young Englishwoman grows less and less able to face the world. Last year she could go out only if someone went with her. Then she could not go out at all, and now we hear that she is too much frightened by her merciless chimeras even to leave her room.

Conversely, a foster mother who lives in the development takes in newborn babies for the Adoption Service because she has three daughters of high-school age and she wants them to have an immediate human responsibility to balance off against the confusions and the too-great ease of American life. There is nothing wrong with that as a piece of independent thinking . . . and in a development, too.

Two streets down the hill, the neat lawns, curved flower beds and marching privet are imperially interrupted by an old residence so completely muffled in vines and masked by untended and overgrown shrubbery that the passer-by can hardly tell a house is standing there. But this Edgar Allan Poe-ish property is not occupied by vampires and revenants. It is occupied by a cheerful and casual family who are completely wrapped up in medieval music and who—playing things like the hautboy—have not yet noticed that the ivy has grown over the ash trays in the living room.

On our street, there is Cynthia; and even the Sine Quas have at least the merit of being oddities. We have divorces and feuds and drinking problems out here in the suburbs, and talent *manqué* and bereavement and sometimes even a little of the joy of life.

I am not going to read any more books by Measurers, I said to Harry at breakfast this morning, no matter how well spoken of. Measurers are an evil influence. By directing everyone's attention so steadily and exclusively to what can be measured ("What do you think of Beowulf's Cake Mix?"—"Whom do you like for President?"), they keep people from being sufficiently aware of what cannot be measured.

Who can tabulate the quiet courage of the man who dropped into the ranks of the Permanent Talented Unemployed and had to sell his house? At least to the outside world, he bore his disaster bravely. Who can measure the influence of a teacher like Mrs. Elliott? Who can delineate the sense of loss and longing of a child whose father dies suddenly of a heart attack at the age of thirty-six?

Conformity? To be sure. A great dreary tundra of physical comfort. A vast and cheerless steppe of pinch pleats, dinettes and political sameness.

But the answer to conformity (I said to Harry at breakfast this morning)—or one of the answers—is not to talk about it so much. The talk, though obviously popular and profitable, just creates more of what it ostensibly deplores.

The other answer to conformity is euthanasia for Measurers. Intending to be "real" and "factual," they inevitably and unavoidably distort; and though they are no doubt kindly people who spend a lot of time with the children, they must go. Their vacant places are needed for playwrights and novelists.

Having thus disburdened myself of a certain amount of hostility for Measurers, I rose from the table and accompanied Harry to the front door. After I had kissed him (my unmeasurable treasure) with perhaps a shade more appreciation and tenderness than usual, I said, "Off you go, Planner. And don't let any graphs grow under your feet."

August 27th ⁓ Eureka! The weather has broken at last and the long-range forecast is that the dog days are over and the climate is back to normal again. Heard the first katydid last night sawing heavily, like a drunken snore, against the buoyant chorus of the crickets, and that is supposed to mean frost in six weeks.

August 29th ⁓ Cynthia and I went in to the city yesterday to see Meinert van Lier and ask whether, since the Women's Liberal Club of Thrumborough would not defy the Legion's threats, there was any way of making the Legion cease threatening. Prior to our appointment, we had both tried to keep the whole matter in a state of suspension in our minds and had not discussed it at length. However, when Cynthia asked me where Meinert van Lier's office is, I found myself replying, "He operates out of a place called the Last Chance Salon."

For my own part, I was pinning my faith to the knowledge and wisdom of the professional. There must be *something* (I felt) that people could do to protect Great-aunt Persis from slanderers and weaklings. A man with Meinert van Lier's experience must be in command of a thousand strategies, and the lay person does not know, because he does not as a rule take the trouble to consult a lawyer, what remedies lie at hand.

As a matter of fact, on the way into town on the train, Cynthia remarked on how strange a thing it seemed, and so unlike the ordinary tenor of our days, for us to be consulting a lawyer.

"It's as if one of us were getting a divorce," she said, "or as if one of our husbands had died and we had an estate to settle."

It seemed less strange to me because six or seven years ago, before Russ and Cynthia had bought their house, our part of town had been threatened by plans for a shopping center of unspeakable size which would have brought thousands of cars a day into the streets at the bottom of the hill. During the period when an embattled citizenry was fighting off this menace, I saw and heard a number of lawyers going through their professional paces, and the experience took them out of the Dickensian pigeonhole they had always occupied in my mind and made them seem alive and modern.

Meinert van Lier came close to putting them back into the pigeonhole. We found him in a building florid with old-fashioned marble, where he has two small rooms crammed with more busts, sectional bookcases and framed group photographs than can be comfortably accommodated. The rooms show signs of improvisation—a window off center, a column half plastered over, dark wainscot giving way suddenly to plywood partitioning.

Meinert van Lier himself is a small man with coarse, reddish skin, a slightly bulbous nose and small eyes that seem even smaller because of the folds of aged flesh draped around them. His appearance is redeemed from the commonplace—indeed, the nearly porcine—by a magnificent crest of thick, fine-spun white hair.

During most of his life he has been a fighter for unpopular causes—an occupation that does not seem to give people the bloom of an apricot espaliered on a sunny wall —and Harry had warned me that he is difficult and touchy. I did not therefore expect him to emanate rays of sunny charm; but I was taken aback, at the beginning, by the extent of his self-absorption.

He gestured with his hand at the two crowded little rooms and said with a sort of angry nostalgia, "My old firm used to have two floors in this building."

His deeply wrinkled face settled into lines of self-pity.

"They moved uptown," he said.

Since I knew from Harry that this move had been made a long time ago and that Meinert van Lier had chosen to remain behind—though urged by all his partners to be the sage, the dean and the ornament of the new quarters —I could think of no reply.

"I'm semi-retired."

I glanced at Cynthia, whose disappointment was clearly visible in her face.

"It's foolish to have this set-up," said Meinert van Lier, "but a man has to get out of the house."

"He's too old!" I thought despairingly, my blind faith in the professional completely evaporated. "He's lost the touch."

But just at that moment, he transformed himself. Suddenly, he began to live up to that magnificent hair and, pulling himself together, he gave us his whole attention. It was a cool attention. His level, impersonal scrutiny was that of a falcon looking for game.

"What's your story?" he asked.

It is a simple story if the listener grasps—as Meinert van Lier did instantly—the principle involved. (I was reminded by contrast of how long it took to get the point across, even partially, to Harry's cousin Eugene.)

Well . . .

I suppose Dr. Aspirin and Mrs. Chancellor had conditioned us to expect hemming and hawing, but Meinert van Lier administered the coup de grâce like a plummeting hawk.

If Great-aunt Persis lived in this country and had ample means, Counselor van Lier said, it would certainly be worth while to have a lawyer write to Jim Afterbirth along the lines Harry had suggested. A politically conservative lawyer would be the best choice, and it would not be too difficult to find one who would be glad to do it.

But with Great aunt Persis's residence abroad, and with no financial resources . . .

If the Legion said, "Go ahead, sue," and no suit was brought, the organization's Un-American Committee would only be encouraged in its activities.

Cynthia and I were flattened like a wheat field after hail.

For one dizzy moment I wondered whether Meinert van Lier's advice was conditioned by his age, and whether this was what he would have said when he was a younger man. But he was right across the desk from me and I could see that for the time being he actually *was* a younger man. This was no idle sentimentalist, admiring himself for his suitably harrowed-up feelings. This was an old pro stating the bald reality.

A small, wistful hope reared up in my disorganized mind, and Meinert van Lier whom, in his alert moments, nothing seemed to escape, answered it even before I got it into words.

"I may die any day."

He parted his puckered and sagging lips, sighed heavily, and closed them again.

"And my son did not choose to follow in my footsteps."

I recalled that Harry had said Meinert van Lier's only son—no spring chicken himself, by this time—had a cushy job as head of a large foundation.

A cough and a hoarseness in the throat obscured what the lawyer said next, but it appeared to be about his son, for it referred to bestowing the spoils of a plundered continent on Navajo scientists and Negro poets.

Cynthia and I could not pull ourselves together.

What went through my mind—and I imagined something very like it going through hers—was the bitter realization of what successful frauds Dr. Aspirin and Mrs. Chancellor were. Dr. Aspirin would go right on being the white knight of juvenile delinquency. He would go right on charming and disarming people with his ruefully humorous remarks about the tribulations of being a liberal.

And Mrs. Chancellor (unmarked by any tattoo) would go right on sitting on daises in her expensive evening gowns, and in a few more seasons—when she had been fifteen years the head of this and twenty years the president of that—they would start giving her scrolls and plaques of non-ferrous metals with the phrase "Human Relations" conspicuously engraved on them.

Oh, to be sure, Mrs. C. would be embarrassed and unhappy for a while at any allusion to Cynthia or Greataunt Persis. She lived among reminders of a dignified past and she was not an arriviste. But she would soon be able to persuade herself that she had had no choice—that she had simply been the unwilling victim of something called "our society" or "the times we live in."

Cynthia and I sat in silence. We were overwhelmed with defeat, and ahead loomed the ironic task, no longer to be postponed, of writing to Cynthia's distinguished kinswoman. In her hand, Cynthia held the now unnecessary envelope that had come from Mrs. Chancellor with the Eternal Impurity list on Great-aunt Persis. The white rectangle looked very conspicuous in the cramped quarters of our tête-à-tête and it caught Meinert van Lier's eye.

"What've you got there?"

Correctly divining that it had a connection with our errand, he reached out his hand.

Cynthia, dully obedient, yielded it to him; but she seemed too full of angry despair to talk, so I explained.

The lawyer turned the envelope over and then stiffened. Instantaneously, however, he made himself relax.

"The envelope isn't open," he said in a level and uninflected voice. "It hasn't been opened."

"No," said Cynthia, and lapsed into silence.

"Cynthia brought it over to my house when it came in the mail," I said.

I felt tired to the point of paralysis and completely unwilling to do any more explaining. Life was ashes on my tongue at the moment, but Meinert van Lier had done us the kindness of seeing us and we owed him enlightenment.

"I must say, we were tempted to open it," I remarked, and hesitated. "We talked and talked."

The light glinting on Counselor van Lier's handsome and silky white crest tended to distract attention from his face; but when I scrutinized his worn-out and used-up old features, they were completely impassive.

"We couldn't help seeing Mrs. Chancellor's reaction to the list." The Kafkaesque world of a few years back, with accusations spraying like the fountains of Versailles, seemed to have returned again, and my mouth felt dry.

"Mrs. Chancellor half believed there was something at least a bit wrong with Great-aunt Persis. Things were written down on paper. A committee of Congress was involved."

I began to feel impatient and angry with Meinert van Lier for not helping me out with at any rate an understanding nod. Then I resolved to get it over with quickly, and plunged ahead.

"It was like pornography. For Mrs. Chancellor. For Cynthia and me, too. Something indecent, and yet something you wanted to see."

I took a breath, remembering the complex of feelings— including a very substantial measure of fright—we had had about that envelope, and then I continued.

"In a way, we knew what it would be. Luncheons she'd spoken at, causes she'd given money to, petitions she'd signed about Loyalist Spain or not lynching Negroes."

I paused.

"The way we finally worked it out," I said, "was that this was a list—whatever was on it—purporting to document something."

Meinert van Lier's wrinkled old eyelids moved in an acknowledgment of interest.

"It was documenting the idea that Cynthia's aunt is not a fit person to speak. Either in a tax-supported building in Thrumborough or a tax-exempt building in our town."

For a second I experienced again in retrospect the sense

of triumph, almost of artistic achievement, Cynthia and I had felt when we finally worked out our line of reasoning.

"Since," I concluded, "we wouldn't have any part of any such idea, in any way, shape or form, there was no reason to look at documentation."

Meinert van Lier consistently sat with his frail body held upright, and he did not now lean back. But he gave the effect of leaning back as he smiled at us and said, "Brava! That was using your heads."

I looked at Cynthia, to share with her the happy circumstance of having finally conquered this grudging old party, but she was sitting grimly chin in hand and clearly had not been following.

"When I think of two *women* sitting around with an unopened envelope for four weeks!" said Meinert van Lier.

He sighed with relish.

"I'll have to re-examine the legend about Pandora's box. In the light of new evidence."

Then, as he handed the envelope back to Cynthia, his mood abruptly collapsed.

"Do you know what they did to me before that Committee?" he asked angrily.

I nodded. Harry had refreshed my dim memory of it. The lawyer had not himself been called, but his whole career had been laughingly brushed aside—by witnesses in a sweat to protect themselves—as insignificant and a matter for amused condescension. The hotheaded intellectual lightweight. The bad-tempered Don Quixote whom we in our superior wisdom tolerate.

It was all of a piece (I came back shatteringly to the reason for our visit) with the indignity about to be inflicted on Great-aunt Persis. The good people persistently discounted, written off as nothing, boorishly handled . . .

The brief, happy interlude of communion was over. Meinert van Lier had fallen back into his original mood of self-preoccupation, and Cynthia and I were face to face with the fact that we had no further recourse. It was almost a physical pain to put ourselves through the ritual of leave-taking, and save for one split-second flash of warmth in the Aztec ruin of the old face—and even that I may have imagined—our thanks were received by the lawyer as unbubblingly as they were given.

When we were outdoors again, I looked around to see if there were any place we could get a drink. Right across the street, a bar was pulsing like Vesuvius with molten neon; but its top hats and musical notations outlined in throbbing red failed to appeal. So did Schrafft's in the next block, demurely signaling in black and gold, "All passion spent." I thought of taking a taxi to some aristocratic caravansary where we could allay the smart of defeat, at least briefly, with thick rugs and well-bred silence. But that would have been too reminiscent of Thrumborough and gracious living unillumined by the doctrine of noblesse oblige.

Lower class, middle class, upper class—there was no sanctuary. We were displaced persons.

On the train, Cynthia suddenly burst out of her silence and exclaimed, "That old man! That Meinert van Lier! He enjoyed telling us there's nothing to do!"

"Oh, no, Cynthia. He envied us our youth. Terribly."

But Cynthia did not hear.

"Why did Harry send us to such an old man? What was he thinking of?"

I bristled.

"There was nothing a younger man could have said," I rejoined tartly, "that Meinert van Lier didn't."

But the next minute I regretted my asperity. I knew what was gnawing at Cynthia. It gnawed at me, too—the feeling that we looked ridiculous. Two middle-class ladies of sheltered habit and a superannuated old civil-rights lawyer. A depressing trio—unheadlined and dully domestic—getting wrought up over something no one else is interested in. The galling thing about a lost cause or a hopeless case, I thought, is its limp weight, the wet-dish-cloth adhesions of its draperies.

I tried to summon up a mental picture of Great-aunt Persis, but she seemed far away, remote and dim. If only we had been sensible, I thought, and drained this cup when it was presented to us, the whole thing would have been forgotten by this time and we would be happy again.

But I knew better than that.

What made Cynthia's and my nerves so raw that we came close to quarreling with each other was an unstated question. How do you keep up to the standards you believe in, how do you keep from getting corrupted, when *nobody* is around to symbolize the higher things?

September 1st ❧ The darkest hour just before the dawn.

Coming into Harry's postage-stamp study tonight, I look at that last entry and am surprised that I could have been so dejected only four evenings ago.

For we made them buy it back, Friend Cynthia and I, and tonight we celebrated. Russ and Cynthia got a sitter for the boys and came to dinner, and we had lobster and drank toasts to Great-aunt Persis—"Aye, tear her tattered ensign down!" Harry said, holding up his glass and laughing—and to Meinert van Lier and to ourselves.

At least, Russ proposed and Russ and Harry both drank a toast to Cynthia and me, and I said that we appreciated it, but that he made us sound exactly like a couple of Albert Payson Terhune collies—"great-souled."

High spirits. That's what we were in.

Washing and drying the good china, however, after Russ and Cynthia had gone, was enough to put Harry's jocund mood under sedation, and he has gone upstairs to bed. But I am still effervescing.

I should, however, begin at the beginning.

The seasonal holiday comes early this year, and when I went into Plethora, Inc. this morning, it looked like an anthill which has just been scuffed by a passing foot. The elderly Negro who sweeps up lettuce leaves with a four-foot-wide broom—his tragic, chattel-slavery countenance conspicuous against the bright packaging—was virtually immobilized by the crowds. Empty cartons were piled up in corners almost to ceiling height, and looking into the dark recesses of the storeroom, where more cartons were coming in on a conveyor belt, one could imagine even the cockroaches running around with aprons on, getting ready for the Labor Day weekend.

I had to wait for a cart, but I did not mind, as I always feel like Gurth the Swineherd when steering one of those ungainly objects. Standing in somewhat vacant and not very happy mood near the door, I suddenly became aware of a radiance more authoritative than the luminous paint on the sign just above me saying FREE! THIS WEEK ONLY!

The non-spurious radiance came from Cynthia, who

was advancing toward me looking like Aurora, the rosy-fingered dawn.

She was alone.

"Where are the boys?" I asked automatically.

"I have a cleaning woman," she said. "Helen, where have you *been*? I called last night till long past a decent hour, and again this morning."

I explained.

Ever since we had seen Meinert van Lier, I had been feeling like something left squarely in the path of Sherman's march to the sea. So, as Cora was spending last night with some old lags from day camp, Harry got the house seats to a play through one of his board members. At the theater, we met friends who asked us to their apartment, where we stayed rather late.

"And this morning," I concluded, "I tried to cure my depression by taking the car and driving out into the country."

"Helen," breathed Cynthia, "Maida Chancellor called me—"

" 'Maida!' " I interrupted. "Since when are we first-naming that monster?"

"It's all right," Cynthia said. "They're going through with it. About Aunt Persis. Just as it was planned."

A little boy who had been doing acrobatics on the rail between the "Out" and "In" doors landed heavily on his back at my feet. He stared up at me for a second, then rolled over and clambered back up on the rail.

I looked at Cynthia. She seemed to be surrounded by an almost visible penumbra of happiness and triumph.

"Oh!"

I flung my arms around her, and a passing matron with a nice face smiled at us.

Backing away, I tried to take in the news.

"They changed their minds?"

Cynthia nodded.

A sense of justice done, of symmetry restored, of a balance redressed flooded over me like a tide. Why, I wondered, do people think of justice as harsh? It is an ichor in the veins, a fragrance in the nostrils . . .

One of the checkers, bringing in a long line of empty carts from the parking lot, came within an inch of pushing his chromium centipede over our toes. I came back from the realms of poesy.

"Did the Legion withdraw its objections?"

Cynthia smiled mischievously.

"I guess not. Mrs. Chancellor said Jim Afterbirth came to her almost with tears in his eyes. 'Don't get me into trouble,' he said."

"But what *happened?*"

"I don't know," Cynthia replied. "Mrs. Chancellor called me on the phone. Not stammering. Almost her old self."

"And—?"

"She said, 'Dear girl . . .' That's what she called me. 'By any wonderful chance have you not yet written to your aunt?'

"Well, of course," Cynthia said, "I was floored to hear from her. But I just said, no, I hadn't written yet."

A fat lady loaded with empty bottles plowed blindly between us.

Cynthia resumed.

"She said the Liberal Club wanted to apologize *abjectly*. They had been too hasty. They hadn't thought things through clearly enough . . ."

"They've had all summer to think clearly. Why now?" Cynthia shrugged.

"Darling, I don't know. I really don't know anything. But she's coming to my house tomorrow afternoon. They have to get cracking on this if they want to make a big thing of it, and she's going to tell me all the plans.

"I'm being treated," Cynthia added impishly, "like royalty."

She sparkled, and indeed I felt a good ten years younger myself. The thought that that shameful discourtesy would not be perpetrated on Great-aunt Persis made me buoyant as a cork.

"I'm delighted," I said, "but I can't understand it. What's behind all this?"

I thought of Meinert van Lier, but he had said he did not know Mrs. Chancellor. Besides, his powers were failing and I doubted whether he would have remembered Cynthia and me two minutes after we left.

An alarming thought struck me.

"Is the Women's Liberal Club," I said to Cynthia, "likely to change back? After all, the Legion hasn't altered its position. The going may be rough."

"I don't think so," Cynthia answered confidently. "Mrs. C. is happy about this. You could hear it in her voice."

I nodded.

"She must have felt a traitor to her class, doing a thing like that to your aunt."

Looking at Cynthia, I was suddenly reminded of Dr. Aspirin and thought to myself, "Swinburne got it upside down. It should have been 'the roses and raptures of virtue—the lilies and languors of vice.' "

Cynthia was saying something about Jim Afterbirth.

". . . he's absolutely frantic. But this time Mrs. Chancellor is plowing *him* under, instead of me."

I shook my head.

"Mrs. C. never came to this by herself. But what could have happened?"

Cynthia smiled a little vaguely.

"Russ," she said, "thinks the Legion won't be able to stir up much fuss. The public mood has changed."

"More shame to the Women's Liberal Club for not standing its ground in the first place."

Then, suddenly, the mention of Russ galvanized me.

"Harry!" I exclaimed. "I have to tell Harry right away."

I glanced over at the phone booth, but it had three small children in it, their nostrils and open mouths flattened against the glass.

"I'll go home and phone," I said. "I don't feel like shopping now. Especially not here."

Tonight for the first time there is a hint of autumnal chill in the air, which is why Harry's study is comfortable instead of stuffy. But the coolness reminded me that I had better go up and see that Cora had at least a sheet over her.

Time never seems to stand so still as when I look at Cora in her bed asleep. But of course it is an illusion. Even as I watch, in the dimness and silence, bone and muscle are building up—the psyche is flexing itself in dreams.

To resume, however . . .

Of all the horrid sensations that man as a social being can experience, perhaps the worst is being caught out in

a lie. But certainly the second worst is to unfurl a resplendent and glittering piece of information and have it
greeted with indifference. How would those fellows have
felt, who brought the good news from Ghent to Aix, if
they had evoked no more than a lackadaisical "Umm"
with their message?

I got Harry on the phone; I burst out with the exciting
development about Great-aunt Persis; and after a moment's pause he said, "Umm."

I was so deflated that compared to me a pricked balloon
would have looked like the Winged Victory. After a moment of complete disorientation—could I have gotten the
wrong Harry Fitzgibbons?—I said, "What's the matter?
Don't you think it's important any more?"

Harry was instantly penitent. "It's just that I'm not as
much surprised as you expected. Because I heard a bit of
gossip on the train this morning."

"What?" I asked sulkily.

"You're going to be pleased," he said. "It seems that
you and Cynthia made a tremendous impression on
Meinert van Lier."

"We did?"

"The evening of the day you saw him, he tottered into
a party at his son's apartment. There was a couple there
from Thrumborough, and when he heard that name, he
started to tell about your visit and said you were a pair of
remarkable young women."

"That's nice." I was mollified. "But—"

"So Mrs. Chancellor probably heard right away that the
story on Great-aunt Persis was getting around."

"Why should she care? She had what she thought was
a good excuse."

"Yes, but this looked serious. You'd been to a lawyer, and the lawyer was Meinert van Lier. A civil-liberties man and a tiger when aroused."

"Well?"

"How was she to know that van Lier had told you there was nothing to be done?"

"*Oh!*" I exclaimed. Illumination flooded in. "And having a guilty conscience anyway, she'd naturally assume that something in the way of punishment was shaping up."

"But that's not all."

There was amusement in Harry's voice.

"I builded better than I knew when I sent you around to van Lier."

He paused, evidently savoring what he had to say.

"Maida Chancellor works in several organizations where she's much more deeply involved than she is with the Women's Liberal Club."

Harry cleared his throat.

"Item," he said. "These organizations need foundation support. Item: van Lier's son is a foundation head."

I was silent. At length I said disappointedly, "What you mean is that Mrs. Chancellor is doing the right thing for the wrong reason."

"Oh, for God's sake!" exclaimed Harry. "Don't look a gift horse in the mouth."

He modulated into a kindlier tone.

"Mrs. Chancellor is doing the right thing because you and Cynthia leaned on her and leaned on her. Finally, something had to give."

All of a sudden, jolted into perceptiveness, perhaps, by Harry's impatience, I realized what had been accomplished. Cynthia and I are going to meet Great-aunt Persis in a setting freed of its burden of ignominy and shame. Who says there are no triumphs in the suburbs?

That was the thought that went through my mind again, later on at the dinner table.

Sometimes the old Biblical phrases, so long familiar, so abstractly admired, spring into life more vividly than any modern counterpart. I looked at the platter of lobster shells, the wine bottle, cypress green and cypress slender, among the candles, and Cynthia with her classical features all irradiate. I thought of Mrs. Chancellor and Dr. Aspirin and Jim Afterbirth and the unknown soldiers of the Legion's State Committee on Un-Americanism. And I knew what the psalmist meant when he said, "Thou preparest a table before me in the presence of mine enemies."

September 15th ❧ It is two weeks since I have set anything down in my diary, and the omission has not been due to the fact that school has started and the P.T.A. has opened up and Cora is a Girl Scout and not a Brownie any more and the political party of my choice (not exactly a closely guarded secret) wants in its local manifestation to get something done about the garbage removal.

None of these things has silenced me, or even all of them in combination. Rather it is that an impulse has spent itself. Whatever it was that moved me to communicate with Ignis Fatuus moves me no longer. The impetus is gone. Besides, the leaves are starting to turn and it is going to be one of those seasons of which Edna Millay said, "Lord, Thou'st made the world too beautiful this year."

With the universe of acorn and inchworm and cobweb so shortly to be closed down for the winter, it is no time for a practicing sensualist to be sitting indoors at a typewriter.

It is no time for a devoted and admiring wife to be sitting at a typewriter either, for Harry worked late tonight and I must get out the car and pick him up at a train which enjoys the courtesy title of the 8:53 local express.

"I can understand the 'local' well enough," I said to Harry. "But . . ."

He interrupted.

"There are two clumps of phlox and a hydrangea bush it doesn't stop at," he said. "Just roars right past. So it's perfectly entitled to be called an express."

I must be off forthwith on the familiar trip down the hill to the station, leaving Young Cat and Old Cat to hold the fort until we get back. They are sitting on the living-room rug, about two feet apart, washing their faces.

Lick, lick, lick, *wipe*.

Lick, lick, lick, *wipe*.

One has the vagrant fancy that it is the self-cleansing rhythm of life itself.

ABOUT ❦ MARGARET HALSEY

Margaret Halsey's own Westchester diary began when she was born—in Yonkers, New York. She was educated in the Yonkers public-school system, at Skidmore College (B.S.) and at Columbia University (M.A.). She first burst on the literary horizon with the publication of With Malice Toward Some *(1938; republished in paperback 1959). There followed the wartime novel* Some of My Best Friends Are Soldiers *(1944) and two studies in American culture,* Color Blind *(1946) and* The Folks at Home *(1952).*

Unlike the city-planner Harry Fitzgibbons of This Demi-Paradise, *Miss Halsey's husband is on the administrative staff of New York University. But she does live in a suburb and she does have a daughter who was once Cora's age.*